D0527558

SCHOLASTIC

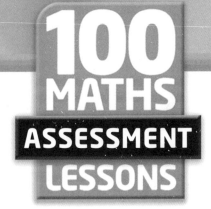

100 MATHS ASSESSMENT LESSONS

TERMS AND CONDITIONS

IMPORTANT – PERMITTED USE AND WARNINGS – READ CAREFULLY BEFORE USING

Licence

YEAR 4

Scottish Primary 5

Minimum specification:
- PC or Mac with a CD-ROM drive and 512 Mb RAM (recommended)
- Windows 98SE or above/Mac OSX.4 or above
- Recommended minimum processor speed: 1 GHz

For all technical support queries, please phone Scholastic Customer Services on 0845 603 9091.

Joan Nield and Lesley Fletcher

CREDITS

Authors
Joan Nield and Lesley Fletcher

Series Consultant
Ann Montague-Smith

Development Editor
Kate Baxter

Editor
Helen Kelly

Assistant Editor
Margaret Eaton

Series Designers
Joy Monkhouse, Micky Pledge and Melissa Leeke

Designer
Quadrum Publishing Solutions

Illustrations
Garry Davies

CD-ROM development
CD-ROM developed in association with Vivid Interactive

Additional material
Transitional tests written by Joan Nield and Lesley Fletcher

Mixed Sources
Product group from well-managed forests and other controlled sources
www.fsc.org Cert no. TT-COC-002769
© 1996 Forest Stewardship Council
FSC

ACKNOWLEDGEMENTS

Extracts from the Primary National Strategy's *Primary Framework for Mathematics* (2006) www.standards.dfes.gov.uk/primaryframework and the Interactive Teaching Programs originally developed for the National Numeracy Strategy © Crown copyright. Reproduced under the terms of the Click Use Licence.

Every effort has been made to trace copyright holders for the works reproduced in this book, and the publishers apologise for any inadvertent omissions.

Published by Scholastic Ltd
Villiers House
Clarendon Avenue
Leamington Spa
Warwickshire CV32 5PR

www.scholastic.co.uk

Designed using Adobe InDesign.

Printed by Bell and Bain Ltd, Glasgow

1 2 3 4 5 6 7 8 9   9 0 1 2 3 4 5 6 7 8

Text © 2009 Joan Nield and Lesley Fletcher

© 2009 Scholastic Ltd

British Library Cataloguing-in-Publication Data
A catalogue record for this book is available from the British Library.

ISBN 978-1407-10192-7

Contents

100 Maths Assessment Lessons

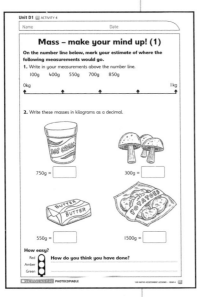

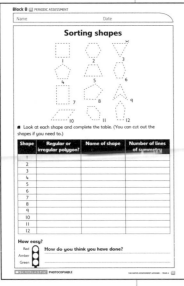

About the series

100 Maths Assessment Lessons is designed to provide assessment opportunities for all children. Linked to the renewed *Primary Framework for Mathematics*, it also supports the implementation of the new *Assessing Pupil's Progress* (APP) guidelines by linking the new APP assessment focuses to the PNS Framework objectives. Each title in the series also provides single-level tests that can be used at the end of a year, or at any point throughout the year, to provide a summary of where, in relation to national standards, learners are at a given point in time. By using the titles in this series, a teacher or school can be sure that they are covering the mathematics curriculum and obtaining relevant data about their children's achievements.

About assessment

100 Maths Assessment Lessons provides a wide range of opportunities for teachers and children to assess progress. There are three different types of assessment identified by the APP guidelines:

Day to day

Day-to-day assessment is an integral and essential part of effective learning and teaching. Teachers and children continually reflect on how learning is progressing, see where improvements can be made and identify the next steps to take. Strategies that should be part of everyday learning and teaching include:
● sharing and talking about learning objectives, learning outcomes and success criteria with children
● observing and listening to gather intelligence
● planning for group talk, peer assessment and self-assessment to help children develop as independent learners.

Periodic assessment

The purpose of periodic assessment is to give an overview of progress and provide diagnostic information about the progress of individual children, linked to national standards. It is intended to be used at regular (half-termly or termly) intervals to provide an overview of performance based on a wide range of evidence. Periodic assessment should be used to:
● make a periodic review of progress and attainment across a whole task
● identify gaps in experience and inform planning
● help learners know and recognise the standards they are aiming for
● involve both learner and teacher in reviewing and reflecting on evidence.

Transitional assessment

Transitional assessment should be used at points of transition which might be from year to year, school to school or level to level. The pupils' progress data from day-to-day assessment and periodic assessment will support the teacher in making decisions about how pupils are likely to perform in transitional assessments. The key characteristics of transitional assessment are:
● it brings together evidence, including tests, to reach a view of attainment

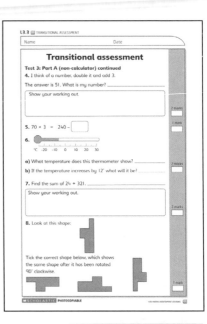

■SCHOLASTIC

- it is externally validated and externally communicated
- it is set within the framework of national standards.

For a complete list of strategies for day-to-day assessment and further information about periodic and transitional assessment, visit the National Strategies website (**http://nationalstrategies.standards.dcsf.gov.uk**).

About this book

This book is set out in the five blocks that form the renewed *Primary Framework for Mathematics*. Each block consists of three units, with each unit containing:
- an overview of the work covered in the unit, including the objectives, assessment focuses and learning outcomes for each activity (end-of-year objectives are denoted in bold text)
- day-to-day assessment activities based upon the assessment for learning and children's learning outcomes for each objective within a unit (note that the using and applying objectives are either incorporated into other assessments, or assessed on their own, depending upon the content and context of the unit)
- periodic assessment activities based on the end-of-year objectives within each unit.

Assessment activities

Each activity contains:
- details of children's expected prior learning before the activity is used
- the relevant objective(s) and vocabulary that children are expected to know
- description of the activity for the teacher or learning support assistant
- group, paired or individual work for the children. Where adult intervention is required, this is explained. Most of the activities include the use of an activity sheet or interactive activity from the CD-ROM
- clear differentiation, to support less confident learners in the group or to extend the learning for the more confident learners
- common misconceptions and how to remediate these
- probing questions to ask the children
- next steps: these are differentiated to help teachers decide how to help children who need further support. Suggestions for further work and references to related Framework units or blocks are given to support or extend the children.

What's on the CD-ROM?

Each CD-ROM contains a wealth of resources. These include:
- **worksheets** with answers, where appropriate, that can be toggled by clicking on the 'show' or 'hide' buttons at the bottom of the screen
- **transitional assessments:** year-appropriate single-level tests, oral tests, mark schemes and instructions
- **general resource sheets** (for example, number grids) designed to support a number of lessons
- **interactive activities:** for individuals or small groups, with in-built marking to assess specific objectives
- **Interactive Teaching Programs:** specific ITPs, originally developed for the National Numeracy Strategy
- **whiteboard tools:** a set of tools (including a pen, highlighter and eraser) that can be used to annotate activity sheets for whole-class lessons. These tools will work on any interactive whiteboard
- **display pages:** some activities require a problem or investigation to be shown to the whole class on an interactive whiteboard. The whiteboard tools can also be used with these images to annotate them as necessary
- **editable planning grids** (in Word format) are available to help teachers integrate the lessons into their planning.

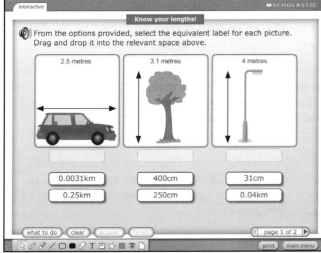

How to use the CD-ROM

System requirements
Minimum specification:
- PC or Mac with a CD-ROM drive and 512 Mb RAM (recommended)
- Windows 98SE or above/Mac OS X.4 or above
- Recommended minimum processor speed: 1 GHz

Getting started
The *100 Maths Assessment Lessons* CD-ROM should auto run when inserted into your CD drive. If it does not, browse to your CD drive to view the contents of the CD-ROM and click on the *100 Maths Assessment Lessons* icon.

From the start-up screen you will find four options: select **Credits** to view a list of acknowledgements. Click on **Register** to register the product in order to receive product updates and special offers. Click on **How to use this CD-ROM** to access support notes for using the CD-ROM. Finally, if you agree to the terms and conditions, select **Start** to move to the main menu.

For all technical support queries, contact Scholastic Customer Services help desk on 0845 6039091.

How to use the materials
The materials contained in the book and on the CD-ROM can be used with one child, a group, or in a whole-class activity. Decide who is ready to be assessed from the daily work that the children complete and from your observations. The CD-ROM allows users to search for resources by block, unit or lesson. Users can also search by Framework objective, assessment focus or by resource type (for example, worksheet, interactive resource, display page or ITP).

Day-to-day assessments
These should be used to support learning. They can be used during a lesson, when you judge that children are ready for an assessment activity. The materials can also be used weekly or after a unit of work has been completed.

Periodic assessments
These can be used with a group of children rather than with the whole class. This could be at the end of a unit of work (for example, at the end of a half-term or term). Decide who is ready to be assessed using the outcomes of the day-to-day assessment activities and your observations of children's performance.

Self-assessment
A self-assessment sheet is provided for you and the children to complete. It can be used where there is no activity sheet, so that there is evidence of the children's confidence in what they have learned and how well they can use that learning. There are 'traffic lights' at the bottom of the sheet that children can shade to show their confidence: red for 'need help'; orange for 'having some understanding'; green for 'go!' (ie the child feels confident with his/her learning).

All the activity sheets also have the traffic light system for the children to record their level of confidence, along with a space for them to write about how easy/hard they found the activity.

Transitional tests
These tests provide evidence of where, in relation to national standards, children are at a given point in time. Photocopiable tests (both written and oral), mark schemes and answer sheets are all available on the CD-ROM.

Class PET
A whole-school version of *100 Maths Assessment Lessons* is available with an expanded range of digital assessment activities, as well as the facility to report, record and track pupil's work. For further information visit the Class PET website, **www.scholastic.co.uk/classpet**.

BLOCK A
Counting, partitioning and calculating

Expected prior learning
Check that children can already:
- identify the calculation needed to solve a word problem
- explain and record their methods and solutions to problems and calculations
- read, write, partition and order whole numbers to 1000
- use £.p notation
- understand and use the < and > signs
- round two- or three-digit numbers to the nearest 10 or 100
- recall addition and subtraction facts for each number to 20
- add or subtract mentally combinations of one- and two-digit numbers
- derive number pairs that total 100
- use informal written methods to add and subtract two- and three-digit numbers
- estimate sums and differences of two- or three-digit numbers
- recall multiplication and division facts for the 2-, 3-, 4-, 5-, 6- and 10-times tables
- multiply one- and two-digit numbers by 10 and 100
- use informal written methods to multiply and divide two-digit numbers
- round remainders up or down, depending on the context.

Objectives overview
The text in this diagram identifies the focus of mathematics learning within the block.

Key aspects of learning
- Problem solving
- Evaluation
- Communication
- Motivation

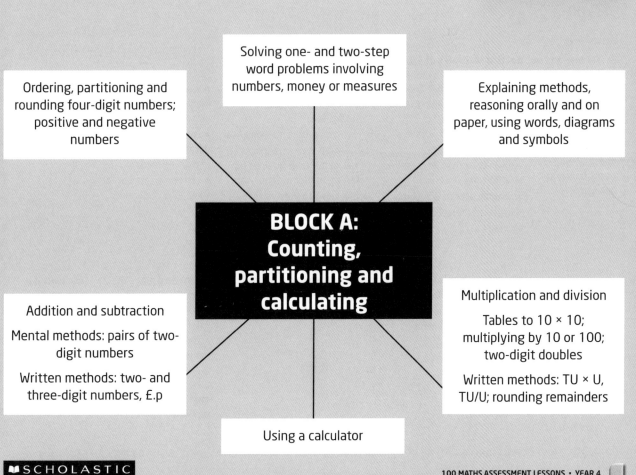

Solving one- and two-step word problems involving numbers, money or measures

Ordering, partitioning and rounding four-digit numbers; positive and negative numbers

Explaining methods, reasoning orally and on paper, using words, diagrams and symbols

BLOCK A: Counting, partitioning and calculating

Addition and subtraction
Mental methods: pairs of two-digit numbers
Written methods: two- and three-digit numbers, £.p

Multiplication and division
Tables to 10 × 10; multiplying by 10 or 100; two-digit doubles
Written methods: TU × U, TU/U; rounding remainders

Using a calculator

Unit 1 ▢ Counting, partitioning and calculating

Introduction

In this unit, children are introduced to the calculator, which is used for checking their calculations. They use the symbols <, > and = in the context of negative numbers. They use estimating, rounding and inverses in order to check calculations. They begin to learn and use the 7-, 8- and 9-times table facts, making use of what they already know from the 2- to 6-times tables. They are encouraged to use diagrams where this will help them to calculate or to display the answers to problems and to explain to others how they solved problems.

Framework objectives	Assessment focuses		Success criteria for Year 4	Learning outcomes
	Level 4	Level 3		
① Four-digit numbers ② Positive and negative numbers				
Partition, round and order four-digit whole numbers; use positive and negative numbers in context and position them on a number line; state inequalities using the symbols < and > (e.g. −3 > −5, −1 < +1)	• recognise and describe number relationships	• understand place value in numbers to 1000, e.g. ○ represent/compare numbers using number lines, 100-squares, base 10 materials, etc. • recognise negative numbers in contexts such as temperature	• able to explain the value of any digit in a four-digit number • can order a range of four-digit numbers • able to use and order negative numbers • can use the symbols < and > to describe inequalities between numbers	I can read, write and put in order four-digit numbers and positive and negative numbers. I can use the < and > signs with positive and negative numbers (e.g. −3 < 1).
③ Adding and subtracting multiples of 10, 100 or 1000				
Report solutions to puzzles and problems, giving explanations and reasoning orally and in writing, using diagrams and symbols	• present information and results in a clear and organised way, e.g. ○ organise written work, e.g. record results in order ○ begin to work in an organised way from the start ○ consider appropriate units ○ use related vocabulary accurately	• discuss their mathematical work and begin to explain their thinking, e.g. ○ use appropriate mathematical vocabulary ○ talk about their findings by referring to their written work • use and interpret mathematical symbols and diagrams	• able to explain method of solving problem • can use appropriate vocabulary when explaining method • can use mathematical symbols and diagrams	I can explain to someone else how I solve problems and puzzles.
Use knowledge of addition and subtraction facts and place value to derive sums and differences of pairs of multiples of 10, 100 or 1000	• use a range of mental methods of computation with addition and subtraction, e.g. ○ calculate complements to 1000	• add and subtract two-digit numbers mentally, e.g. ○ calculate 36 + 19, 63 − 26	• can use a range of mental methods to quickly add multiples of 10, 100 or 1000 • can use a range of mental methods to quickly find the difference between multiples of 10, 100, or 1000	I can work out sums and differences of multiples of 100 or 1000.

Unit 1 Counting, partitioning and calculating

Framework objectives	Assessment focuses		Success criteria for Year 4	Learning outcomes
	Level 4	Level 3		
(4) Adding two-digit numbers mentally				
Add or subtract mentally pairs of two-digit whole numbers (e.g. 47 + 58, 91 − 35)	• use a range of mental methods of computation with addition and subtraction	• add and subtract two-digit numbers mentally, e.g. ○ calculate 36 + 19, 63 − 26	• can add two-digit numbers mentally • can subtract two-digit numbers mentally	*I can add and subtract two-digit numbers in my head (e.g. 26 + 47, 43 − 16).*
(5) Multiplication and division facts for 8				
Recognise and continue number sequences formed by counting on or back in steps of constant size	• recognise and describe number patterns, e.g. ○ continue sequences	• recognise a wider range of sequences, e.g. ○ recognise sequences of multiples of 2, 5 and 10	• able to describe and make a sequence of numbers by counting on or back	*I can count on and back in eights.*
Derive and recall multiplication facts up to 10 × 10, the corresponding division facts and multiples of numbers to 10 up to the tenth multiple	• quickly derive division facts that correspond to multiplication facts up to 10 × 10 • recall multiplication facts up to 10 × 10 and quickly derive corresponding division facts	• derive associated division facts from known multiplication facts, e.g. ○ given a number sentence, use understanding of operations to create related sentences • use mental recall of the 2, 3, 4, 5 and 10 multiplication tables	• knows facts for 8- and 9-times tables • can give an associated division fact for multiplications in the 8- and 9-times table	*I know my 8-times table and my 9-times table.*
(6) Multiplying and dividing by 10 or 100				
Multiply and divide numbers to 1000 by 10 and then 100 (whole-number answers), understanding the effect; relate to scaling up or down	• use place value to multiply and divide whole numbers by 10 or 100	• understand place value in numbers to 1000, e.g. ○ use understanding of place value to multiply/divide whole numbers by 10 (whole number answers)	• can multiply whole numbers by 10 or 100 • can divide whole numbers by 10 or 100 • able to explain what happens to digits when multiplying or dividing by 10 or 100	*I can multiply and divide by 10 and 100. I can explain what happens to the digits when I do this.*
(7) Devilish doubles				
Identify the doubles of two-digit numbers; use these to calculate doubles of multiples of 10 and 100 and derive the corresponding halves	• recognise and describe number relationships • use inverse operations	• add and subtract two-digit numbers mentally • use mental recall of the 2 multiplication table	• can double two-digit numbers • can calculate doubles of multiples of 10 or 100 • can derive halves of known doubles	*I can double two-digit numbers.*

Unit 1 📖 Counting, partitioning and calculating

Framework objectives	Assessment focuses		Success criteria for Year 4	Learning outcomes
	Level 4	Level 3		
⑧ Calculators for problems				
Use a calculator to carry out one-step and two-step calculations involving all four operations; recognise negative numbers in the display, correct mistaken entries and interpret the display correctly in the context of money	● solve problems with or without a calculator, e.g. ● solve two-step problems choosing appropriate operations ● deal with two constraints simultaneously ● interpret a calculator display of 4.5 as £4.50 in context of money ● carry out simple calculations involving negative numbers in context ● check the reasonableness of results with reference to the context or size of numbers	● use mental recall of addition and subtraction facts to 20 in solving problems involving larger numbers, e.g. ● choose to calculate mentally, on paper or with apparatus ● solve one-step whole number problems appropriately ● solve two-step problems that involve addition and subtraction	● uses addition and subtraction facts to 20, when solving problems ● can solve one- or two-step problems using a calculator	*I can use a calculator to help me solve one-step and two-step problems. I know how to enter prices such as £1.29 and £2.30 into a calculator. I know that −7 on a calculator means negative 7.*
Use knowledge of rounding, number operations and inverses to estimate and check calculations	● use inverse operations, e.g. ● use a calculator and inverse operations to find missing numbers ● check the reasonableness of results with reference to the context or size of numbers	● solve whole number problems including those involving multiplication or division that may give rise to remainders, e.g. ● identify appropriate operations to use ● round up or down after simple division, depending on context	● uses rounding to estimate and check calculations	*I can estimate and check the result of a calculation.*

Activity ①

Prior learning
Children can read, write, partition and order whole numbers to 1000.

Framework objective
Partition, round and order four-digit whole numbers; use positive and negative numbers in context and position them on a number line; state inequalities using the symbols < and > (for example, −3 > −5, −1 < +1)

Vocabulary
explain, predict, pattern, relationship, rule, sequence, place value, partition, thousands, digit, four-digit number, compare, order, round

Resources
Interactive activity: Four-digit numbers
Resource sheets: Self-assessment, 0-9 digit cards (one set per pair of children)

① Four-digit numbers

Use the interactive activity 'Four-digit numbers'. Choose different children to click on the numbers, read them and then drag them into their correct positions in the list of numbers. Work through both screens with different children, asking probing questions. Once they have completed this, give each pair of children a set of 0-9 digit cards. Each child chooses four cards and writes down the four-digit numbers that they can make. Then they each write their numbers in order of size, explaining their reasoning to their partner. Ask the children to say the highest/lowest number they can make, and explain how they know. Decide whether to use the self-assessment sheet for the children to record their achievements and what they need to do next.

Teacher support
Less confident learners: Ask pairs of children to choose three cards to make three-digit numbers, and then order them. Ask: *What is the highest/lowest number you can make from these digits?*
More confident learners: Ask pairs to choose five cards to make five-digit numbers, and then order them. What is the highest/lowest number they can make from these digits?

Common misconceptions
Children do not know what each digit represents.
Use place value cards to make three- and then four-digit numbers. Use these numbers to discuss the value of each digit and develop children's understanding.

Probing questions
● How do you know this is the highest number?
● What is this number rounded to the nearest 10/100? What rule did you use?
● 4361 = 4000 + ☐ + 60 + 1. What is the missing number? How do you know?

Next steps
Support: Order and partition three-digit numbers and ensure that children are confident with these. This can be repeated several times to ensure that the children understand the vocabulary. See also Year 3 Block E Unit 3.
Extension: Generate all possible numbers using four given digits, including those using zero as a place holder; order a mixed set of three-digit and four-digit numbers. See also Year 4 Block A Unit 2.

Activity ②

Prior learning
Children can read, write, partition and order whole numbers to 1000. They understand and use the < and > signs.

Framework objective
Partition, round and order four-digit whole numbers; use positive and negative numbers in context and position them on a number line; state inequalities using the symbols < and > (for example, −3 > −5, −1 < +1)

Vocabulary
positive, negative, above/below zero, compare, order, greater than (>), less than (<), equal to (=), degrees Celsius (°C)

Resources
Interactive activity (ITP): Thermometer
Worksheet: Positive and negative numbers
Resource sheets: Self-assessment, 0–20 numeral cards
Classroom resources: whiteboards and pens, cards showing '> means greater than' and '< means less than'

② Positive and negative numbers

Use the ITP 'Thermometer'. Set the maximum to 30, the minimum to −10 and the interval to 1. Start with the temperature at 9°. Ask a child to read the temperature. Choose another child and ask them where the slider button would be if the temperature went down 10°. Move the slider button to show the answer. Choose different children to answer questions such as: *What would the temperature be if it went down/up another 3°? Which temperature is higher, −5° or −9°?* Ask the children to record their answers on their individual whiteboards, using > or <. Decide whether to use the self-assessment sheet for the children to record their achievements and what they need to do next.

Teacher support
Less confident learners: Work with a small group. Use cards showing '> means greater than' and '< means less than' to help the children remember what the symbols mean.
More confident learners: Work with a small group. Use the interactive activity 'Thermometer' as above, but with the interval set to 2. Work through questions as above.

Common misconceptions
Children do not understand that higher numbers mean higher temperatures. Show children on the thermometer that, as the temperature goes down, the negative number increases.

Probing questions
● The temperature was −2° last night. The temperature is now 8° higher. What is the temperature now?
● Use < or > to complete this number sentence: −7 ☐ −11.

Next steps
Support: Give children practice using < and > symbols when comparing numbers 0 to 20: for example, ask them to put down two numeral cards, and write the correct symbol between them. See also Year 2 Block A Unit 3.
Extension: Use the worksheet 'Positive and negative numbers'. See also Year 4 Block A Unit 3.

Activity ③

Prior learning
Children can recall addition and subtraction facts for each number to 20. They can derive number pairs that total 100.

Framework objective
● Use knowledge of addition and subtraction facts and place value to derive sums and differences of pairs of multiples of 10, 100 or 1000
● Report solutions to puzzles and problems, giving explanations and reasoning orally and in writing, using diagrams and symbols

Vocabulary
pattern, relationship, rule, place value, partition, digit, add, subtract, total, difference, plus, minus, multiple

Resources
Interactive activity: Partition numbers
Worksheets: Adding and subtracting multiples of 10 or 100, Adding and subtracting multiples of 10, 100 or 1000
Resource sheets: Self-assessment, 10-100 numeral cards, 1-9 digit cards
Classroom resources: whiteboards and pens

③ Adding and subtracting multiples of 10, 100 or 1000

Use the interactive activity 'Partition numbers'. Type 60 into the blank box at the top of the screen, then click 'make'. The 6 and the 0 digits can be dragged apart (click on the small arrow in the top left corner of each card to reveal its value). Repeat to make a 30 card. Ask: *What is the sum of these two numbers? How did you work it out? What is the difference between these two numbers?* Repeat for two more tens numbers. Use the tabs on the left-hand side of the screen to move on to three-digit and four-digit numbers. Repeat for 700 and 500 (and other hundreds numbers), and then for 7000 and 5000 (and other thousands numbers). Ask the children to record their answers on their whiteboards and show their answers. Ask them to explain the pattern. Decide whether to use the self-assessment sheet for the children to record their achievements and what they need to do next.

Teacher support
Less confident learners: Ask these children to challenge a partner to add/subtract pairs of number cards (multiples of 10 only).
More confident learners: Ask these children to add/subtract three numbers that are multiples of 100/1000.

Common misconceptions
Children do not see the link between adding pairs of single-digit numbers and adding multiples of 10, 100 or 1000.
Use 1-9 digit cards. Ask a child to choose two cards (for example, 3 and 6). *What is 3 + 6? What is 30 (3 tens) + 60 (6 tens)?* Repeat for hundreds and thousands.

Probing questions
● How could you work out what 600 and 700 is?
● How do you know that the difference between 8000 and 3000 is 5000? What did you use to help you?

Next steps
Support: Ask the children to complete the worksheet 'Adding and subtracting multiples of 10 or 100'. See also Year 3 Block E Unit 1.
Extension: Ask the children to complete the worksheet 'Adding and subtracting multiples of 10, 100 or 1000'. See also Year 3 Block E Unit 1.

BLOCK A

Activity ④

Prior learning
Children can recall addition and subtraction facts for each number to 20. They can add or subtract mentally combinations of one- and two-digit numbers.

Framework objective
Add or subtract mentally pairs of two-digit whole numbers (for example, 47 + 58, 91 − 35)

Vocabulary
calculate, calculation, answer, method, explain, relationship, partition, digit, add, subtract, sum, total, difference, plus, minus

Resources
Display page: Adding two-digit numbers mentally
Resource sheet: Self-assessment
Classroom resources: dominoes (one set between four children), tens and units from base ten equipment, whiteboards and pens

④ Adding two-digit numbers mentally

Reveal the display page 'Adding two-digit numbers mentally'. Invite a child to choose a domino and ask them to derive a two-digit number from it (for example, a 5 and a 4 could make 54). Invite another child to do the same with another domino. Ask the rest of class to add the two two-digit numbers and write the answer on their whiteboards. Repeat several times to check the children's understanding of addition before going on to check subtraction using the same procedure. Decide whether to use the self-assessment sheet for the children to record their achievements and what they need to do next.

Teacher support
Less confident learners: Work with small groups. Provide tens and units from base ten equipment, for children to use to help them count on from the larger number when adding. For example, for 34 + 27, they take 2 ten towers and 7 units. Start at 34 and count on 2 tens and then 7 units, using the equipment. Check that the children can add 10 and multiples of 10 to a two-digit number.
More confident learners: Ask these children to choose three dominoes, make three two-digit numbers and add them. They should record their numbers and answers on their whiteboards, and should be able to explain how they arrived at their answers.

Common misconceptions
Children mix up tens or units digits when adding/subtracting.
Use base ten equipment to make numbers and record each stage of calculation (see 'Less confident learners' above).

Probing questions
● What do you add to 63 to get 98? How could you record that as a number sentence?
● Work out 72 − 35. How did you do it?
● How do you know that the answer to 85 − 44 cannot be 45?

Next steps
Support: Practise adding on 10 and multiples of 10, before going on to add two two-digit numbers. Let the children use a 100-square to check their answers if needed. See also Year 3 Block D Unit 2.
Extension: Try adding a two-digit number to a three-digit number, mentally. Check the answer by subtracting the two-digit number from the three-digit number. See also Year 4 Block A Unit 2.

■SCHOLASTIC

Activity ⑤

Prior learning
Children can explain and record their methods and solutions to problems and calculations. They can recall multiplication and division facts for the 2-, 3-, 4-, 5-, 6- and 10-times tables.

Framework objectives
● Recognise and continue number sequences formed by counting on or back in steps of constant size
● **Derive and recall multiplication facts up to 10 × 10, the corresponding division facts and multiples of numbers to 10 up to the tenth multiple**

Vocabulary
predict, reason, reasoning, pattern, relationship, rule, sequence, add, subtract, count on/back, multiply, divide, product, pattern, multiple

Resources
Interactive activity: Multiplication and division facts for 8
Worksheet: Multiplication facts for 8
Resource sheet: 1–9 digit cards

⑤ Multiplication and division facts for 8

Use the interactive activity 'Multiplication and division facts for 8'. Ask a child to start before the first square at top left, count on 8, and reveal the number. *What number would we land on if we counted on another 8? Show me. What number would we land on if we counted on two more lots of 8?* Repeat the activity, with different children revealing other multiples of 8. Ask the children to work in pairs to find two multiplications and two divisions for one of the revealed numbers. Repeat for other multiples of 8. This activity could also be used for other times tables.

Teacher support
Less confident learners: Ask these children to work in pairs to complete the activities on the worksheet 'Multiplication facts for 8'.
More confident learners: Ask children to write a multiplication and division calculation for each multiple of 8 on the screen. Repeat for other times tables.

Common misconceptions
Children do not understand the link between multiplication and division.
Display a number line showing 10 jumps of 8. Demonstrate that the jumps going right show a multiplication (for example, 5 lots of 8 is 40), and that the jumps coming back show a division – for example, 40 divided by 5 jumps is 8.

Probing questions
● What number would you land on if you counted on 3 lots of 8? How do you know?
● What multiplication can you make using 8 and 32? What related division can you make?
● How would knowing 3 × 4 help you to work out 3 × 8?

Next steps
Support: Use cards from the worksheet 'Multiplication facts for 8' to practise the 8-times table. The children can create their own sets of cards for the 9-times table and practise with those. See also Year 3 Block E Unit 3.
Extension: Use 1–9 digit cards. Children choose a card, multiply the number by 8 or 9 and write down the number sentence. They then find the related division. See also Year 4 Block A Unit 2.

BLOCK A

Activity ⑥

Prior learning
Children can multiply one- and two-digit numbers by 10 and 100.

Framework objective
Multiply and divide numbers to 1000 by 10 and then 100 (whole-number answers), understanding the effect; relate to scaling up or down

Vocabulary
answer, method, explain, predict, reason, reasoning, pattern, relationship, rule, place value, partition, digit, multiply, divide, product, multiple

Resources
Interactive activity: Bingo: times tables (×10 and ×100)
Worksheet: Multiplying and dividing by 10 or 100
Resource sheet: Bingo cards

⑥ Multiplying and dividing by 10 or 100

Hand out copies of the worksheet 'Multiplying and dividing by 10 or 100' and asks the children to complete it.

Teacher support
Less confident learners: Ask these children to work in pairs to discuss and work out each problem.
More confident learners: Encourage these children to check their answers on a calculator.

Common misconceptions
Children do not understand that multiplying by 100 is the same as multiplying by 10 twice.
Use a place value table for thousands, hundreds tens and units. Write in 37 and ask children to multiply it by 10. Discuss where to write the answer (370). Emphasise that multiplying by 10 moves each digit to the next column because it increases each digit's value. *Multiply 370 by 10 and write the answer on the table.* Write 37 again and ask children to multiply it by 100. Show that the answers to 37 × 10 × 10 and 37 × 100 are the same.

Probing questions
● How would you change £26.42 into pence?
● Why does 24 × 100 give the same answer as 240 × 10?
● What happens to the digits when I multiply/divide by 100?

Next steps
Support: Print out copies of the bingo cards (either from the interactive activity 'Bingo: times tables (×10 and ×100)', or use the blank cards available on the CD-ROM). Provide each pair of children with a bingo card. Ask them to work together to write a ×10 or a ×100 multiplication for each number. They could then write a ÷10 or a ÷100 division for each number. See also Year 3 Block E Unit 2.
Extension: Print out the required number of bingo sheets from the CD-ROM. Provide each pair of children with a blank bingo card. Groups of four children can use the interactive activity 'Bingo: times tables' to play a game of bingo. See also Year 4 Block A Unit 2.

Activity ⑦

Prior learning
Children can read, write, partition and order whole numbers to 1000. They can add or subtract mentally combinations of one- and two-digit numbers.

Framework objective
Identify the doubles of two-digit numbers; use these to calculate doubles of multiples of 10 and 100 and derive the corresponding halves

Vocabulary
relationship, rule, place value, partition, estimate, approximately

Resources
Display page: Devilish doubles
Resource sheets: Self-assessment, 1-9 digit cards
Classroom resources: whiteboards and pens, place value arrow cards (tens and units)

⑦ Devilish doubles

Reveal the display page 'Devilish doubles'. Ask individual children to come to the board and write in the correct doubles of the green numbers. Ask: *How did you work that out? Why was 76 tricky?* As children fill in each answer, the rest of the class can write answers on their own whiteboards. Ask the children what they would need to do to work out the missing green numbers on the board. (Halve the white numbers.) Choose individual children to do these. Decide whether to use the self-assessment sheet for the children to record their achievements and what they need to do next.
Answers: 62 → 124, 24 → 48, 53 → 106, 76 → 152, 146 → 73, 128 → 64, 240 → 120, 102 → 51.

Teacher support
Less confident learners: Use 1–9 digit cards. Ask the children to choose two cards to make a two-digit number, and then double it.
More confident learners: Use 1–9 digit cards. Ask the children to choose two cards to make a two-digit number, multiply it by 10 and by 100, and then double all three numbers. For example, 24, 240, 2400 becomes 48, 480, 4800.

Common misconceptions
Children do not partition numbers before doubling or halving.
Practise partitioning two-digit numbers using place value cards. Then double/halve each part of the number, and combine the parts to make the double/half.

Probing questions
● If double 24 is 48, what is double 240 or double 2400? How do you know?
● What is half of 62? Half of 620? Half of 6200? Explain how you worked that out.

Next steps
Support: Repeat the activity, this time making each number using place value arrow cards. Then double/halve each part of the number. See also Year 3 Block D Unit 3.
Extension: Ask children in pairs to write a two-digit even number, and then halve this number. Say: *Multiply your original number by 10 and halve it. Multiply your original number by 100 and halve it.* For example, 46 and 23, 460 and 230, 4600 and 2300. See also Year 4 Block B Unit 2.

Activity ⑧

Prior learning

Children can identify the calculation needed to solve a word problem. They can explain and record their methods and solutions to problems and calculations. They can estimate sums and differences of two- or three-digit numbers and round remainders up or down, depending on the context.

Framework objectives
● Use a calculator to carry out one-step and two-step calculations involving all four operations; recognise negative numbers in the display, correct mistaken entries and interpret the display correctly in the context of money
● Use knowledge of rounding, number operations and inverses to estimate and check calculations

Vocabulary
calculator, display, key, enter, clear, constant, problem, solution, calculate, calculation, operation, answer, method, explain, add, subtract, multiply, divide, estimate, round

Resources
Display page: Calculators for problems
Worksheets: Calculators for problems (1), (2) and (3)
Resource sheet: Self-assessment
Classroom resources: calculators (individual and demonstration)

⑧ Calculators for problems

Reveal the display page 'Calculators for problems'. Ask the children to work in pairs within teams of four. Pair A should work together to estimate the answer to question 1, while Pair B should use calculators to answer question 1. Can Pair A beat the calculator? Ask pairs to swap over to tackle question 2. Decide whether to use the self-assessment sheet for the children to record their achievements and what they need to do next.

Teacher support
Less confident learners: Ask these children to work in pairs with adult support to solve the questions on the worksheet 'Calculators for problems (1)'. The first question is a one-step problem.
More confident learners: Ask these children to work in pairs to input their own numbers on the worksheet 'Calculators for problems (2)', to create their own problems and solve them.

Common misconceptions
Children do not break the problem down into parts.
Encourage children to list what they need to do in order to solve the problem: identify what the problem is asking for; identify the number of steps and operations needed; carry out the calculations; give the answer to the problems.

Probing questions
● Explain how you estimated your answer. Can you suggest a way to make this estimate more accurate?
● What did you have to input on your calculator? If the answer was 32.4, what did this mean in £ and p?

Next steps
Support: Ask the children to work in pairs to input their own numbers on the worksheet 'Calculators for problems (2)', to create their own problems and solve them, for further practice. See also Year 3 Block D Unit 1.
Extension: Ask these children to complete the worksheet 'Calculators for problems (3)' for further practice. See also Year 3 Block E Unit 2.

Unit 2 ⬜ Counting, partitioning and calculating

Introduction
In this unit children explain their methods and reasoning orally and on paper, using words, diagrams and symbols. They continue to order, partition and round four-digit numbers and positive and negative numbers. They use mental methods of addition and subtraction for pairs of two-digit numbers and written methods for two- and three-digit numbers (including money). Children continue to practise multiplication and division (tables to 10 × 10), multiplying by 10 or 100, two-digit doubles, written methods for TU × U and TU ÷ U, and rounding remainders.

Framework objectives	Assessment focuses		Success criteria for Year 4	Learning outcomes
	Level 4	Level 3		
① Name that decimal!				
Use decimal notation for tenths and hundredths and partition decimals; relate the notation to money and measurement; position one-place and two place decimals on a number line	• order decimals to three decimal places	• begin to use decimal notation in contexts such as money, e.g. ○ order decimals with one dp, or two dp in context of money ○ know that £3.06 equals 306p	• able to explain the value of each digit in a decimal number • can order decimal numbers	*I can use decimals when I work with money and measurement.*
② How did you do that?				
Report solutions to puzzles and problems, giving explanations and reasoning orally and in writing, using diagrams and symbols	• present information and results in a clear and organised way, e.g. ○ begin to work in an organised way from the start ○ use related vocabulary accurately	• discuss their mathematical work and begin to explain their thinking • use and interpret mathematical symbols and diagrams	• uses number lines to demonstrate additions and subtractions • able to explain methods using appropriate vocabulary	*I can explain how I solve problems, using diagrams and symbols to help me.*
Add or subtract mentally pairs of two-digit whole numbers (e.g. 47 + 58, 91 − 35)	• use a range of mental methods of computation with addition and subtraction	• add and subtract two-digit numbers mentally, e.g. ○ calculate 36 + 19, 63 − 26	• uses a range of methods to add mentally pairs of two-digit numbers • uses a range of methods to subtract mentally pairs of two-digit numbers	*I can add and subtract mentally pairs of two-digit numbers and find a difference by counting on.*
③ Adding and subtracting large numbers				
Refine and use efficient written methods to add and subtract two- and three-digit whole numbers and £.p	• use efficient written methods of addition and subtraction e.g. ○ calculate 1202 + 45 + 367 or 1025 − 336	• add and subtract three-digit numbers using written methods, e.g. ○ add and subtract decimals in the context of money, where bridging is not required	• can use an efficient written method to add or subtract two and three-digit numbers	*I can add and subtract three-digit numbers using a written method.*

Unit 2 ◻ Counting, partitioning and calculating

Framework objectives	Assessment focuses		Success criteria for Year 4	Learning outcomes
	Level 4	Level 3		
④ Number patterns				
Recognise and continue number sequences formed by counting on or back in steps of constant size	● recognise and describe number patterns, e.g. 　● continue sequences	● recognise a wider range of sequences, e.g. 　● recognise sequences of multiples of 2, 5 and 10	● can describe and make a sequence of numbers by counting on or back	*I can count on and back in sevens.*
⑤ Tricky tables				
Derive and recall multiplication facts up to 10 × 10, the corresponding division facts and multiples of numbers to 10 up to the tenth multiple	● quickly derive division facts that correspond to multiplication facts up to 10 × 10 ● recall multiplication facts up to 10 × 10 and quickly derive corresponding division facts	● derive associated division facts from known multiplication facts, e.g. 　● given a number sentence, use understanding of operations to create related sentences ● use mental recall of the 2, 3, 4, 5 and 10 multiplication tables	● can multiply a one-digit number and multiple of 10 by 7, 8 or 9 ● can derive a division from a multiple of 7, 8 or 9	*I know my tables to 10 × 10.* *I can use the multiplication facts I know to work out division facts.*
⑥ Magic multiples				
Multiply and divide numbers to 1000 by 10 and then 100 understanding the effect; relate to scaling up or down	● use place value to multiply and divide whole numbers by 10 or 100	● understand place value in numbers to 1000, e.g. 　● use understanding of place value to multiply/divide whole numbers by 10 (whole number answers)	● can multiply numbers to 1000 by 10 or 1000 ● can divide multiples of 10 or 100	*I can multiply and divide numbers by 10 or 100 and describe what happens to the digits.*
⑦ Estimating, multiplying and dividing				
Develop and use written methods to record, support and explain multiplication and division of two-digit numbers by a one-digit number, including division with remainders (e.g. 15 × 9, 98 ÷ 6)	● use efficient written methods of short multiplication and division	● multiply and divide two-digit numbers by 2, 3, 4 or 5 as well as 10 with whole number answers and remainders, e.g. 　● calculate 49 ÷ 3	● uses an efficient written method to multiply a two-digit number by a one-digit number ● uses an efficient written method to divide a two-digit number by a one-digit number	*I can multiply and divide a two-digit number by a one-digit number.*
Use knowledge of rounding, number operations and inverses to estimate and check calculations	● use inverse operations, e.g. 　● use a calculator and inverse operations to find missing numbers ● check the reasonableness of results with reference to the context or size of numbers	● solve whole number problems including those involving multiplication or division that may give rise to remainders	● uses rounding up/down to estimate the answers to calculations ● uses estimates to check results of calculations	*I can estimate and check the result of a calculation.*

Activity ①

Prior learning
Children can use £.p notation and can read, write, partition and order whole numbers to 1000.

Framework objective
Use decimal notation for tenths and hundredths and partition decimals; relate the notation to money and measurement; position one-place and two-place decimals on a number line

Vocabulary
decimal point, decimal place, tenths, hundredths, pound (£), penny/pence (p), compare, order

Resources
Interactive activity: Name that decimal!
Worksheets: Name that decimal! (1) and (2)
Resource sheet: 0-9 digit cards
Classroom resources: £1, 10p and 1p coins, whiteboards and pens

① Name that decimal!

Reveal the interactive activity 'Name that decimal!'. Move one of the markers to 0.6 on the number line. Ask the children to write the decimal on their whiteboards. Repeat for other decimals. Sometimes say: *Write this in £.p. How many pence is this?* (For example, 0.6 = 60p or 2.3 = £2.30.) Next, click on the tab on the left-hand side of the screen to move to the next screen showing a different number line. Move the marker to about 0.13. Ask the children to estimate the decimal and write it to two places. Repeat for other decimals. Invite the children to write the final two decimals in £.p.

Teacher support
Less confident learners: Work through the activity with a small group. Make sure that the children are confident with decimals to one place (tenths) before progressing to decimals to two places (hundredths).
More confident learners: Hand out the worksheet 'Name that decimal! (1)' and give each pair of children a set of 0-9 digit cards. Ask the children to take it in turns to pick two cards and use them to form a decimal with the digit 3 (for example, they could use 5 and 4 to make the decimal 3.54). They should mark the decimal on the decimal number line. Repeat several times.

Common misconceptions
Children think that numbers with more digits are higher numbers.
Use a number line to demonstrate the relative positions of different decimal numbers or ask children to make up a number using pounds and pence. Ask: *Is 1.27 or 1.5 greater? Would you prefer to have £1.27 or £1.50?*

Probing questions
● Tell me what the 6 digit represents in 3.46.
● Which is larger, 4.15 or 4.5? How do you know?

Next steps
Support: Give these children £1 and 10p, and later 1p coins. Ask them to make up several decimals to one place and then decimals to two places, using these coins. For example, 2.3 = 2 × £1 and 3 × 10p coins. See also Year 3 Block A Unit 1.
Extension: Hand out copies of the worksheet 'Name that decimal! (2)' and ask the children to complete it in pairs. See also Year 4 Block A Unit 3.

Activity ②

Prior learning
Children can explain and record their methods and solutions to problems and calculations. They can recall addition and subtraction facts for each number to 20. They can add or subtract mentally combinations of one- and two-digit numbers.

Framework objectives
● Report solutions to puzzles and problems, giving explanations and reasoning orally and in writing, using diagrams and symbols
● **Add or subtract mentally pairs of two-digit whole numbers (for example, 47 + 58, 91 − 35)**

Vocabulary
problem, solution, calculate, calculation, equation, operation, answer, method, explain, predict, reason, reasoning, pattern, relationship, rule, partition, digit, add, subtract, sum, total, difference, plus, minus

Resources
Interactive activity: Maths Boggle
Resource sheets: Blank number lines, Self-assessment

② How did you do that?

Display these additions and subtractions on the board: 28 + 43; 59 + 64; 42 + 92; 87 + 53; 94 − 63; 81 − 37; 75 − 69. Ask the children to work in pairs. They should take it in turns to do each calculation mentally and then demonstrate the method they used on the blank number lines, explaining their reasoning. Explain that they should be looking for easy ways to do each calculation mentally. Decide whether to use the self-assessment sheet for the children to record their achievements and what they need to do next.

Teacher support
Less confident learners: Work with these children as a group and discuss strategies together for each calculation.
More confident learners: Invite these children to write additions and subtractions involving a three-digit number and a two-digit number for a partner to work out.

Common misconceptions
Children do not see patterns or strategies.
Give children a check list of strategies/patterns to look for (for example, making 10, identifying doubles or near doubles, finding differences, and rounding up/down to nearest 10).

Probing questions
● What strategy did you use to help you work out 59 + 64? Did anyone do it differently?
● You found that the difference between 75 and 69 was 6. Can you think of other pairs of two-digit numbers with a difference of 6?

Next steps
Support: Ask small groups of children to practise adding/subtracting a one-digit number to/from a two-digit number, and discuss with them the patterns or strategies that they could use for each calculation. See also Year 3 Block D Unit 2.
Extension: In pairs or two teams, let these children play the interactive activity 'Maths Boggle', highlighting two numbers each time to either add or subtract. See also Year 4 Block A Unit 3.

Activity ③

Prior learning
Children can use £.p notation. They can use informal written methods to add and subtract two-digit and three-digit numbers.

Framework objective
Refine and use efficient written methods to add and subtract two-digit and three-digit whole numbers and £.p

Vocabulary
calculate, calculation, operation, answer, method, place value, partition, thousands, digit, add, subtract, sum, total, difference, plus, minus, pound (£), penny/pence (p)

Resources
Worksheets: Adding and subtracting large numbers (1) and (2)
Classroom resources: base ten equipment

③ Adding and subtracting large numbers

Ask the children to complete the worksheet 'Adding and subtracting large numbers (1)'.

Teacher support
Less confident learners: Work through the activity with small groups of children. Use base ten equipment, if necessary, to help with the calculations.
More confident learners: Include calculations that involve adding and subtracting four-digit numbers, or adding three three-digit numbers.

Common misconceptions
Children are unable to partition large numbers before adding/subtracting.
Use base ten equipment to make each number before doing calculations.

Probing questions
● How does partitioning help us to calculate 537 + 329?
● What is wrong with this calculation? 254 + 398 = 642

Next steps
Support: Give these children further practice adding two and three two-digit numbers before progressing to calculations involving three-digit numbers. See also Year 3 Block E Unit 3.
Extension: Ask these children to complete the worksheet 'Adding and subtracting large numbers (2)'. This worksheet could also be adapted so that children first add the numbers and then find the difference between them. See also Year 4 Block A Unit 3.

BLOCK A

Activity ④

Prior learning
Children can explain and record their methods and solutions to problems and calculations.

Framework objective
Recognise and continue number sequences formed by counting on or back in steps of constant size

Vocabulary
predict, reason, reasoning, pattern, relationship, rule, sequence, add, subtract, count on/back

Resources
Worksheets: Number patterns (1), (2) and (3)
Resource sheet: 100-square
Classroom resources: Interlocking cubes

④ Number patterns

Provide each child with a copy of the worksheet 'Number patterns (1)'. Ask the children to continue each sequence in the grid on the sheet.

Teacher support
Less confident learners: Give each pair of children a 100-square, and explain that they can use it to count on/back from given numbers in each sequence.
More confident learners: Give these children the worksheet 'Number patterns (2)' so that they can create their own sequences with three numbers. They can challenge each other to continue the sequences.

Common misconceptions
Children do not count on/back accurately or lose count.
Provide children with interlocking cubes. Explain that they are going to count forwards and backwards in steps of 7, and ask them to make a tower of seven cubes. To find 7 more/less than 35, ask children to 'put 35 in their heads' and to count on/back on the cubes; 35 (in head), 34, 33, 32, 31, 30, 29, 28 (on each cube).

Probing questions
● What do you notice about numbers that are multiples of 4 or 8? Could 37 be a multiple of 4 or 8? Why?
● How can the multiples of 4 help us find multiples of 8?
● I count on three 7s from 14. What number do I reach?

Next steps
Support: Give the children more practice in finding further patterns, counting on/back in steps of different sizes each time. See also Year 3 Block E Unit 3.
Extension: Challenge the children to complete the worksheet 'Number patterns (3)'. See also Year 4 Block A Unit 3.

Activity ⑤

Prior learning
Children can recall multiplication and division facts for the 2-, 3-, 4-, 5-, 6- and 10-times tables.

Framework objective
Derive and recall multiplication facts up to 10 × 10, the corresponding division facts and multiples of numbers to 10 up to the tenth multiple

Vocabulary
multiply, divide, product, pattern, multiple, problem, solution, calculation, explain, relationship, remainder, multiple

Resources
Interactive activities: Tricky tables, Dominoes
Resource sheets: Multiplication square, 10–100 numeral cards, 0–9 digit cards

⑤ Tricky tables

Display the interactive activity 'Tricky tables'. In this activity the children choose digit cards and drag and drop them to make the correct answers to a range of multiplication and division questions.

Teacher support
Less confident learners: Let these children work in pairs and use a multiplication square as an aid to finding answers, if needed.
More confident learners: Ask these children to work in pairs, and place the multiples of 10 cards and the digit cards face down in separate piles. They take it in turn to pick one card from each pile and multiply the numbers together (for example, 5 × 30).

Common misconceptions
Children do not understand the link between multiplication and division facts. Demonstrate by creating an array on squared paper and asking the children to write down the multiplication and division facts associated with it. For example, the array should below could be described by 4 × 3 = 12, 3 × 4 = 12, 12 ÷ 3 = 4, 12 ÷ 4 = 3.

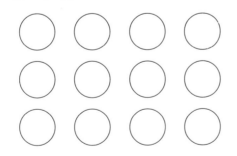

Probing questions
● 3 × 4 is 12. How can that help me work out 6 × 4?
● Write two multiplication and two division facts, using the numbers 56, 7 and 8.
● 6 × 8 is 48. What is 6 × 80 and 6 × 800? How do you know?

Next steps
Support: Ask the children to work in pairs or small groups. Using 0–9 digit cards, practise one multiplication table each session. For example, for the 3-times table, pick a card, and ask the children to give the product of the number and 3. See also Year 4 Block A Unit 1.
Extension: Ask pairs or small teams to play the interactive activity 'Dominoes'. See also Year 4 Block A Unit 3.

BLOCK A

Activity ⑥

Prior learning
Children can multiply one-digit and two-digit numbers by 10 and 100.

Framework objective
Multiply and divide numbers to 1000 by 10 and then 100 (whole-number answers), understanding the effect; relate to scaling up or down

Vocabulary
answer, method, explain, predict, reason, reasoning, pattern, relationship, rule, place value, partition, digit, multiply, divide, product, multiple

Resources
Interactive activity: Magic multiples
Worksheet: Magic multiples
Classroom resources: 10-100 numeral cards, dice

⑥ Magic multiples

Display the interactive activity 'Magic multiples'. In this activity the children are required to choose the correct answer to each question from a range of options provided. Invite them to think of a rule that would help them when multiplying/dividing by 10 or 100.

Teacher support
Less confident learners: Ask these children to work in small groups as they answer the questions on the interactivity activity. Discuss with them what happens when a number is multiplied or divided by 10 or 100.
More confident learners: Ask these children to work in pairs. Each child should write a list of three four-digit numbers that are multiples of 100 and three two-digit numbers, and then exchange lists with their partners. They multiply each two-digit number by 10 and by 100, and they divide each four-digit number by 10 and by 100. Ask them to find a rule for multiplying/dividing by 10/100.

Common misconceptions
Children do not understand the movement of digits when multiplying or dividing.
Demonstrate by writing 67 on the board. Ask the children to multiply by 10. Write the answer under 67. *What has happened to the 6 digit? What has happened to the 7 digit?* Repeat for multiplying by 100 and dividing a hundreds number by 10 or 100. Summarise at the end with: *What happens to each digit when I multiply by 10/100? What happens to each digit when I divide by 10/100?*

Probing questions
● What calculation would you use to change 6700 to 67?
● How many tens are there in 700? How many hundreds are there in 7000?
● What is 500 × 6? How did you work that out?

Next steps
Support: Let these children work in a small group. Provide each group with 'multiples of 10' numeral cards and a dice. Each child chooses a card and shakes the dice. They multiply both numbers together. Can they write a division using the same numbers? See also Year 4 Block A Unit 1.
Extension: Ask these children to complete the worksheet 'Magic multiples' for a further challenge. See also Year 4 Block A Unit 3.

BLOCK A

Activity ⑦

Prior learning

Children can estimate sums and differences of two- or three-digit numbers. They can round remainders up or down. They can recall multiplication and division facts for the 2-, 3-, 4-, 5-, 6- and 10-times tables. They can multiply one- and two-digit numbers by 10 and 100, and use written methods to multiply and divide two-digit numbers.

Framework objectives
● **Develop and use written methods to record, support and explain multiplication and division of two-digit numbers by a one-digit number, including division with remainders (for example, 15 × 9, 98 ÷ 6)**
● Use knowledge of rounding, number operations and inverses to estimate and check calculations

Vocabulary
answer, method, explain, predict, reason, reasoning, pattern, relationship, rule, place value, partition, digit, multiply, divide, product, multiple, quotient, remainder, estimate, round, inverse

Resources
Worksheets: Estimating, multiplying and dividing (1) and (2)
Resource sheet: Self-assessment
Classroom resources: squared paper, place value arrow cards

⑦ Estimating, multiplying and dividing

Before the lesson, write the following number sentences on the board: 16 × 5; 34 × 6; 87 ÷ 6, 78 ÷ 7. Cover, then reveal the sentences one at a time. Ask the children to work in pairs to first estimate each answer, then use a written method to work out the exact answer. Provide squared paper for the children to record their working out. Choose a pair of children. Ask one child to demonstrate their estimate and the other to demonstrate how they worked out the answer. Repeat for each multiplication/division. Decide whether to use the self-assessment sheet for the children to record achievements and next steps.

Teacher support
Less confident learners: Working in a group, encourage these children to use place value cards to make up each number, before partitioning and multiplying/dividing.
More confident learners: Ask these children to multiply/divide three-digit numbers after first estimating the answers.

Common misconceptions
Children have difficulty rounding up/down to provide accurate estimates. Provide practice in rounding up/down a range of two-digit numbers.

Probing questions
● How did rounding up/down each number help you with your estimate? How did your estimate help you to check the answer to your written calculation?
● Why did you partition 34 before multiplying it?
● Do all divisions have remainders? Which do not?

Next steps
Support: Ask the children to complete the worksheet 'Estimating, multiplying and dividing (1)'. See also Year 3 Block E Unit 3.
Extension: Ask the children to complete the worksheet 'Estimating, multiplying and dividing (2)'. See also Year 4 Block A Unit 3.

Unit 3 ▢ Counting, partitioning and calculating

Introduction

In this unit children solve one- and two-step word problems involving numbers, money or measures. They explain their methods and reasoning, orally and on paper, using words, diagrams and symbols. They continue to order, partition and round positive and negative four-digit numbers. They use mental addition and subtraction for pairs of two-digit numbers and written methods for pairs of two- and three-digit numbers (including money). Children also multiply and divide, including tables up to 10 × 10, multiplying by 10 or 100 and two-digit doubles. They use written methods to multiply and divide two-digit numbers by one-digit numbers and they round remainders.

Framework objectives	Assessment focuses		Success criteria for Year 4	Learning outcomes
	Level 4	Level 3		
① Puzzling problems				
Solve one-step and two-step problems involving numbers, money or measures, including time; choose and carry out appropriate calculations, using calculator methods where appropriate	● solve problems with or without a calculator ● solve two-step problems, choosing appropriate operations ● deal with two constraints simultaneously ● interpret a calculator display of 4.5 as £4.50 in context of money ● carry out simple calculations involving negative numbers in context	● use mental recall of addition and subtraction facts to 20 in solving problems involving larger numbers, e.g. ● choose to calculate mentally, on paper or with apparatus ● solve one-step whole number problems appropriately ● solve two-step problems that involve addition and subtraction	● solves one-step problems using a range of calculations ● solves two-step problems using a range of calculations ● knows when it is appropriate to use a calculator to solve problems	*I can work out how to solve problems with one or two steps.* *I can choose what calculation to work out and I can decide whether a calculator will help me.*
Use a calculator to carry out one-step and two-step calculations involving all four operations; recognise negative numbers in the display, correct mistaken entries and interpret the display correctly in the context of money	● solve problems with or without a calculator ● solve two-step problems, choosing appropriate operations ● deal with two constraints simultaneously ● interpret a calculator display of 4.5 as £4.50 in context of money ● carry out simple calculations involving negative numbers in context ● check the reasonableness of results with reference to the context or size of numbers	● use mental recall of addition and subtraction facts to 20 in solving problems involving larger numbers, e.g. ● choose to calculate mentally, on paper or with apparatus ● solve one-step whole number problems appropriately ● solve two-step problems that involve addition and subtraction	● can use a calculator to solve one- and two-step problems ● can interpret calculator displays	*I know that when I am working with money, 5.4 on a calculator display means £5.40.*
② Number pattern detectives				
Recognise and continue number sequences formed by counting on or back in steps of constant size	● recognise and describe number patterns, e.g. ● continue sequences	● recognise a wider range of sequences, e.g. ● recognise sequences of multiples of 2, 5 and 10	● can describe and make a sequence of numbers by counting on or back	*I can count on and back using negative numbers.*

Unit 3 📖 Counting, partitioning and calculating

Framework objectives	Assessment focuses		Success criteria for Year 4	Learning outcomes
	Level 4	Level 3		
③ Number lines				
Partition, round and order four-digit whole numbers; use positive and negative numbers in context and position them on a number line; state inequalities using the symbols < and > (e.g. −3 > −5, −1 < +1)	• recognise and describe number relationships	• understand place value in numbers to 1000, e.g. ○ represent/compare numbers using number lines, 100-squares, base 10 materials, etc. • recognise negative numbers in contexts such as temperature	• able to explain the value of any digit in a four-digit number • can order a range of four-digit numbers • can use and order negative numbers • can use the symbols < and > to describe inequalities between numbers	*I can read, write and put in order positive and negative numbers. I can use the < and > signs with positive and negative numbers (e.g. −3 < 1).*
④ Money cards				
Use decimal notation for tenths and hundredths and partition decimals; relate the notation to money and measurement; position one-place and two-place decimals on a number line	• order decimals to three decimal places	• begin to use decimal notation in contexts such as money, e.g. ○ order decimals with one dp, or two dp in context of money ○ know that £3.06 equals 306p	• understands the link between decimal notation and money • can order two-place decimals on a number line	*I know how to use decimal notation to write numbers such as one and one tenth, two and three tenths, three hundredths. I can write two pounds forty pence and three pounds seven pence using decimal points. I can put three numbers written in decimal notation in the correct places. on a number line.*
⑤ Sums and differences				
Add or subtract mentally pairs of two-digit whole numbers (e.g. 47 + 58, 91 − 35)	• use a range of mental methods of computation with addition and subtraction	• add and subtract two-digit numbers mentally, e.g. ○ calculate 36 + 19, 63 − 26	• can add pairs of two-digit numbers mentally • can subtract pairs of two-digit numbers mentally	*I can add and subtract mentally any two-digit numbers you give me, such as 56 + 22, 58 + 39, 64 − 37, 98 − 89.*
Use knowledge of rounding, number operations and inverses to estimate and check calculations	• use inverse operations, e.g. ○ use a calculator and inverse operations to find missing numbers • check the reasonableness of results with reference to the context or size of numbers	• solve whole number problems, e.g. ○ identify appropriate operations to use	• uses rounding, estimating and inverses to check answers	*I can estimate and check the result of a calculation.*

Unit 3 ▢ Counting, partitioning and calculating

Framework objectives	Assessment focuses		Success criteria for Year 4	Learning outcomes
	Level 4	Level 3		
⑥ Recording additions and subtractions				
Refine and use efficient written methods to add and subtract two-digit and three-digit whole numbers and £.p	● use efficient written methods of addition and subtraction e.g. ● calculate 1202 + 45 + 367 or 1025 − 336	● add and subtract three-digit numbers using written methods, e.g. ● use written methods that involve bridging 10 or 100 ● add and subtract decimals in the context of money, where bridging is not required	● can use column addition to add two- and three-digit numbers ● can use written method to subtract two- and three-digit numbers	*I can add and subtract two-digit and three-digit numbers using a written method.*
⑦ Tables bingo				
Derive and recall multiplication facts up to 10 × 10, the corresponding division facts and multiples of numbers to 10 up to the tenth multiple	● quickly derive division facts that correspond to multiplication facts up to 10 × 10 ● recall multiplication facts up to 10 × 10 and quickly derive corresponding division facts	● derive associated division facts from known multiplication facts, e.g. ● given a number sentence, use understanding of operations to create related sentences ● use mental recall of the 2, 3, 4, 5 and 10 multiplication tables	● quickly recalls multiplication tables to 10 × 10 ● can work out division facts from multiplication facts	*I know my tables to 10 × 10. I can use the multiplication facts I know to work out division facts.*
⑧ Grid multiplication ⑨ Division challenge				
Develop and use written methods to record, support and explain multiplication and division of two-digit numbers by a one-digit number, including division with remainders (e.g. 15 × 9, 99 ÷ 6)	● use efficient written methods of short multiplication and division	● multiply and divide two-digit numbers by 2, 3, 4 or 5 as well as 10 with whole number answers and remainders, e.g. ● calculate 49 ÷ 3	● can multiply two-digit numbers by one-digit numbers using a grid method ● can use a written method to divide a two-digit number by a one-digit number, including remainders	*I can multiply and divide a two-digit number by a one-digit number.*

Activity ①

Prior learning
Children can identify the calculation needed to solve a word problem. They can explain and record their methods and solutions to problems and calculations.

Framework objectives
● Solve one-step and two-step problems involving numbers, money or measures, including time; choose and carry out appropriate calculations, using calculator methods where appropriate
● Use a calculator to carry out one-step and two-step calculations involving all four operations; recognise negative numbers in the display, correct mistaken entries and interpret the display correctly in the context of money

Vocabulary
problem, solution, calculate, calculation, operation, answer

Resources
Worksheets: Puzzling problems (1), (2), (3) and (4)
Classroom resources: calculators (one per child)

① Puzzling problems

Provide calculators for each child. Ask the children to complete the worksheet 'Puzzling problems (1)' individually.

Teacher support
Less confident learners: Work with small groups. Encourage the children to tackle the problems in pairs, with your support. Break each problem down into stages to help the children understand what they have to do to work out the answers.
More confident learners: Provide the worksheet 'Puzzling problems (2)'. The children can substitute their own numbers and prices into each problem and then give them to a partner to solve.

Common misconceptions
Children cannot decide which operation to use.
Discuss the problem in pairs or small groups and break it down into parts. Discuss strategies, with adult support. Children can work in pairs to write number sentences to reflect each part of the problem.

Probing questions
● How do you know whether you need to add, subtract, multiply or divide? What clues do you look for?
● How did you decide what to do first?
● What would the display of 1.2 mean if you were working with pounds?

Next steps
Support: Ask these children to complete the worksheet 'Puzzling problems (3)'. See also Year 3 Block D Unit 1.
Extension: Provide these children with the worksheet 'Puzzling problems (4)' and ask them to complete it. See also Year 4 Block B Unit 1.

BLOCK A

Activity ②

Prior learning
Children can explain and record their methods and solutions to problems and calculations.

Framework objective
Recognise and continue number sequences formed by counting on or back in steps of constant size

Vocabulary
explain, predict, pattern, relationship, rule, sequence, count on/back

Resources
Resource sheets: Number tracks, Self-assessment
Classroom resources: calculators (one per child), counters, dice, place value arrow cards

② Number pattern detectives

Ask the children to use the constant function on their calculators to create number sequences, each containing four numbers, and to record these on the resource sheet 'Number tracks'. At least one sequence must involve negative numbers. The children should then swap their sheets with a partner and use their calculators to find the rule and the next three numbers for each sequence. Decide whether to use the self-assessment sheet for the children to record their achievements and what they need to do next.

Teacher support
Less confident learners: Ask these children to work in pairs within groups of four. Each pair creates a sequence and challenges the other pair to find the rule and continue the sequence. They should concentrate on sequences that involve counting up in steps of 10 or less.
More confident learners: These children can create sequences in steps of any number, but each sequence must have at least one negative number.

Common misconceptions
Children begin to count on/back from the starting number, instead of the next number.
Use a number square or track. Encourage children to put a counter on the actual number, which they then move each time they count on/back.

Probing questions
● Your pattern counts back in steps of 7. Where would I land if I counted back 4 more steps of 7? How do you know?
● This pattern starts at –13. If I continued to count back, what would my next number be, in this sequence?

Next steps
Support: Help the children become accustomed to patterns with negative numbers by giving them plenty of practice in creating sequences within the range of 5 to –20. See also Year 4 Block A Unit 2.
Extension: Use place value arrow cards to create a three-digit number. Shake a dice and create a sequence counting on/back, using the number thrown, from the three-digit number chosen. See also Year 5 Block 1 Unit 1.

Activity ③

Prior learning
Children can read, write, partition and order whole numbers to 1000, and they understand and use the < and > signs.

Framework objective
Partition, round and order four-digit whole numbers; use positive and negative numbers in context and position them on a number line; state inequalities using the symbols < and > (for example, $-3 > -5$, $-1 < +1$)

Vocabulary
explain, predict, pattern, relationship, rule, sequence, place value, partition, thousands, digit, four-digit number, compare, order, round, positive, negative, above/below zero, compare, order, greater than (>), less than (<), equal to (=)

Resources
Interactive activity: Number lines
Resource sheets: Self-assessment, -1 to -9 digit cards
Classroom resources: whiteboards and pens

③ Number lines

Show screen 1 of the interactive activity 'Number lines'. Ask the children to write the numbers in order on their whiteboards. *What would each number be, rounded to the nearest 10?* Choose different children to drag each number to its correct position on the number line, so they can check their answers. Repeat for other screens. While screen 2 is displayed, point to different digits and ask the children to state their values. Choose two numbers from the screens and ask the children to write them on their whiteboards and insert the appropriate symbol (> or <) between them. Decide whether to use the self-assessment sheet for the children to record their achievements and what they need to do next.

Teacher support
Less confident learners: Work through the activity with a small group of children.
More confident learners: Ask these children to write three other numbers that lie between two numbers shown on the screen.

Common misconceptions
Children have difficulty recognising > or < and using them appropriately.
Ask the children to imagine each symbol is an open mouth. The mouth always eats (is open towards) the bigger number. For example, for $-5 \square -9$ the appropriate symbol is >. The symbol opens towards -5, the greater number. This shows that -5 is greater than -9.

Probing questions
● What numbers could go in the blank spaces to make these statements correct? $\square + \bigcirc < 30$; $40 > \square - \bigcirc$
● Write a statement using two negative numbers and the 'less than' symbol.
● Write a statement using a positive number, a negative number and the 'greater than' symbol.

Next steps
Support: Encourage the children to write more number statements using > or < symbols. See also Year 3 Block A Unit 3.
Extension: Provide sets of -1 to -9 number cards for pairs of children. Each child takes it in turns to pick a card. They then have to choose the appropriate symbol to go between numbers. See also Year 5 Block A Unit 1.

Activity ④

Prior learning
Children can use £.p notation. They can read, write, partition and order whole numbers to 1000.

Framework objective
Use decimal notation for tenths and hundredths and partition decimals; relate the notation to money and measurement; position one-place and two-place decimals on a number line

Vocabulary
decimal point, decimal place, tenths, hundredths, pound (£), penny/pence (p), compare, order

Resources
Resource sheets: Self-assessment, Money cards (one set for each group of four)
Classroom resources: coins (at least 3 × £1, 7 × 10p and 5 × 1p coins for each group of four)

④ Money cards

Ask the children to work in groups of four. Give each group a set of cards made from the resource sheet 'Money cards' and a set of coins. Tell the children to shuffle the cards and place them face down. Each child takes it in turn to pick a card and make that value in £1, 10p and 1p coins. When each child has had two turns, the children can work as a group to order their money cards from smallest value to highest value. Decide whether to use the self-assessment sheet for the children to record their achievements and what they need to do next.

Teacher support
Less confident learners: Ask these children to take one card each and order the cards when everyone has had a turn. Repeat for another round of cards.
More confident learners: Let these children have a third round and then incorporate those cards into the number line already created by the cards.

Common misconceptions
Children do not understand the link between place value and money (for example, they don't understand that 0.7 = 70p).
Write column headings for hundreds (£), tens and units. Children can practise writing amounts under these headings and then matching the amounts with coins.

Probing questions
● What does this card (for example, £2.75) say? What does the digit 7 stand for? How much is it worth?
● Which of these cards is worth the most money? How do you know? Show me, using these coins.

Next steps
Support: Work with the children in small groups. Show them a range of numbers featuring one-place decimals and ask them to read them off to you. See also Year 4 Block A Unit 2.
Extension: Ask the children to work in pairs. Each child writes three two-place decimal numbers between 1 and 9, and then gives them to a partner to order. Together they order both sets of numbers, and describe the value of particular digits to each other. See also Year 4 Block D Unit 2.

Activity ⑤

Prior learning
Children can recall addition and subtraction facts for each number to 20. They can add or subtract mentally combinations of one- and two-digit numbers. They can estimate sums and differences of two- or three-digit numbers, and round remainders up or down, depending on the context.

Framework objectives
● **Add or subtract mentally pairs of two-digit whole numbers (for example, 47 + 58, 91 − 35)**
● Use knowledge of rounding, number operations and inverses to estimate and check calculations

Vocabulary
calculate, calculation, answer, method, explain, relationship, partition, digit, add, subtract, sum, total, difference, plus, minus, remainder, estimate, round, inverse

Resources
Worksheet: Sums and differences
Classroom resources: 0-100 number line (horizontal), base ten equipment (tens and units), dice, place value arrow cards (hundreds, tens and units; one set per pair)

⑤ Sums and differences

Ask the children to work in pairs to complete the worksheet 'Sums and differences'.

Teacher support
Less confident learners: Work with small groups. Encourage the children to separate the tens from the units before calculating (partitioning).
More confident learners: Ask these children to use hundreds place value arrow cards, as well as tens and units, when completing the worksheet 'Sums and differences'.

Common misconceptions
Children do not round up/down accurately.
Display a horizontal 0-100 number line. Point to a two-digit number. Ask children to state which multiple of 10 the number is nearest to. Remind them that if the units digit is 5 or over, then the number is nearest to the next multiple of 10.

Probing questions
● How could estimating tell you that 34 and 59 could not be about 80?
● Why did finding the difference between your total and one of your numbers help you to check your answer?
● Explain how you found the sum of 56 and 27. What helped you?

Next steps
Support: Repeat the activity, using tens and units from base ten equipment. See also Year 4 Block A Unit 2.
Extension: Repeat the activity using two dice to create numbers. See also Year 4 Block D Unit 1.

BLOCK A

Activity ⑥

Prior learning
Children can use £.p notation. They can use informal written methods to add and subtract two- and three-digit numbers.

Framework objective
Refine and use efficient written methods to add and subtract two-digit and three-digit whole numbers and £.p

Vocabulary
calculate, calculation, operation, answer, method, place value, partition, thousands, digit, add, subtract, sum, total, difference, plus, minus, pound (£), penny/pence (p)

Resources
Worksheets: Recording additions and subtractions (1) and (2)
Classroom resources: squared paper

⑥ Recording additions and subtractions

Before the lesson starts, complete the worksheet 'Recording additions and subtractions (1)' on the board, but misalign numbers in the columns so that the answers are incorrect. Hide this working out. Now ask the children to complete the worksheet 'Recording additions and subtractions (1)'. When they have finished, show your examples and use them when asking probing questions. Next, write two of the numbers from the worksheet as amounts of money (for example, £8.32 and 63p). Ask the children to use written methods to find the total and the difference: *What do you have to remember when using written methods for money?*

Teacher support
Less confident learners: Ask these children to work in pairs, and to add two numbers from different columns.
More confident learners: Invite these children to be 'experts' and to explain to a less confident learner how they completed a calculation.

Common misconceptions
Children do not line up the columns when recording numbers.
Provide squared paper. Give children a list of two-, three- and four-digit numbers and ask them to record them as one list, in columns, aligning digits with the same place value.

Probing questions
● Explain how you would record 6306 + 385 + 27. Why would it be useful to estimate the answer first?
● Look at this calculation. What have I done wrong? What should I have done to avoid this?

Next steps
Support: If necessary, give the children more practice in adding two three-digit numbers together, before introducing four-digit numbers. See also Year 4 Block A Unit 2.
Extension: Ask the children to complete the worksheet 'Recording additions and subtractions (2)' with a partner. See also Year 4 Block D Unit 2.

Activity ⑦

Prior learning
Children can recall multiplication and division facts for the 2-, 3-, 4-, 5-, 6-, 8-, 9- and 10-times tables.

Framework objective
Derive and recall multiplication facts up to 10 × 10, the corresponding division facts and multiples of numbers to 10 up to the tenth multiple

Vocabulary
multiply, divide, product, pattern, multiple, problem, solution, calculation, explain, relationship, remainder, multiple

Resources
Interactive activity: Tables bingo
Resource sheets: Self-assessment, 1–9 digit cards

⑦ Tables bingo

Ask the children to work in pairs to play the interactive activity 'Tables bingo'. Before they start, set the timer to five seconds. When they have completed the game, decide whether to use the self-assessment sheet for the children to record their achievements and what they need to do next.

Teacher support
Less confident learners: Let these children play the interactive game with adult support. Before play, set the timer to ten seconds.
More confident learners: These children can play the interactive bingo game as individuals.

Common misconceptions
Children are unable to recall multiplication and division facts quickly.
Provide frequent practice of multiplication tables by playing games and conducting quizzes.

Probing questions
- The product of two numbers is 81. What are those numbers?
- 6 × 8 = 48. What is 7 × 8?
- What is 10 times 8 × 9? How did you work it out?

Next steps
Support: Provide two sets of 1–9 digit cards for each pair. Children take it in turns to choose a card from each pile, and then multiply the two numbers together. See also Year 4 Block A Unit 2.
Extension: Print out some bingo cards from the interactive activity. Provide each child with a card and ask: *How many multiplications/divisions can you find for each number on your card?* See also Year 4 Block B Unit 1.

Activities ⑧ and ⑨

Prior learning
Children can recall multiplication and division facts for the 2-, 3-, 4-, 5-, 6- and 10-times tables. They can multiply one- and two-digit numbers by 10 and 100, and use written methods to multiply and divide two-digit numbers.

Framework objective
Develop and use written methods to record, support and explain multiplication and division of two-digit numbers by a one-digit number, including division with remainders (for example, 15 × 9, 98 ÷ 6)

Vocabulary
answer, explain, predict, reason, pattern, relationship, rule, place value, partition, digit, multiply, divide, product, multiple, quotient, remainder

Resources
Worksheets: Grid multiplication (1), (2) and (3); Division challenge (1) and (2)
Resource sheet: Multiplication square (for support)
Classroom resources: whiteboards and pens

⑧ Grid multiplication

Ask the children to complete the worksheet 'Grid multiplication (1)'.

Teacher support
Less confident learners: Let children use a multiplication square to help them.
More confident learners: Invite these children to write word-related problems.

Common misconceptions
Children are unable to recall multiplication and division facts quickly.
Provide frequent practice of multiplication tables using games and quizzes.

Probing questions
● Which multiplications could you do mentally? Which would you do on paper?
● Would you use a mental or a written method to work out 27 × 8?

Next steps
Support: Ask these children to complete the worksheet 'Grid multiplication (2)'.
Extension: Ask the children to complete the worksheet 'Grid multiplication (3)'.

⑨ Division challenge

Ask the children to complete the worksheet 'Division challenge (1)'.

Teacher support
Less confident learners: Let these children work in pairs, with adult support.
More confident learners: Ask children to write some related word problems.

Common misconceptions
Children do not know the link between division and subtraction.
Use a number line to demonstrate division as repeated subtractions.

Probing questions
● What is the largest remainder if you divide by 7? How do you know?
● When finding answers, how did you know whether to round up or down?

Next steps
Support: Provide further experience of similar problems, until the children are secure with division. See also Year 4 Block A Unit 2.
Extension: Provide these children with the worksheet 'Division challenge (2)'. See also Year 4 Block D Unit 2.

Units 1,2&3 ◾ Periodic assessment

These activities can be used at any time during the teaching of this block to assess those children that you think have achieved the objective. A grid highlighting the related assessment focuses and expected learning outcomes for each activity can be found on the CD-ROM.

Adding and subtracting two-digit numbers mentally

Framework objective
Add or subtract mentally pairs of two-digit whole numbers (for example, 47 + 58, 91 − 35)

Learning outcome
● I can add and subtract mentally any two-digit numbers you give me, such as 56 + 22, 58 + 39, 64 − 37, 98 − 89, and find a difference by counting on.

Provide each child with a copy of the worksheet 'Adding and subtracting two-digit numbers mentally'. Ask the children to work individually to answer the questions, adding and subtracting two-digit numbers and explaining their methods. Alternatively, you could deliver this test orally and ask the children to write their answers on paper.

Products game

Framework objective
Derive and recall multiplication facts up to 10 × 10, the corresponding division facts and multiples of numbers to 10 up to the tenth multiple

Learning outcomes
● I know my 8-times table and my 9-times table.
● I can use the multiplication facts I know to work out division facts.

Ask the children to work in pairs. Provide each pair with a copy of the worksheet 'Products game', together with counters and a set of 1–9 digit cards. After completion of the game, invite each child to choose a multiple of 8 from the grid and to write two divisions using the number 8. Once they have done this, repeat for a multiple of 9.

Multiplication and division pairs

Framework objective
Develop and use written methods to record, support and explain multiplication and division of two-digit numbers by a one-digit number, including division with remainders (for example, 15 × 9, 98 ÷ 6)

Learning outcomes
● I can multiply and divide a two-digit number by a one-digit number.
● I know how to interpret a remainder.

Ask the children to complete the worksheet 'Multiplication and division pairs'. Choose individual children to explain the methods and strategies they used for the multiplications and divisions. Ask questions such as: *How did you decide whether to round up/down if there was a remainder? Can you create a division that would not have a remainder? How did you choose that number?*

Name	Date

Adding and subtracting two-digit numbers mentally

Answer these questions in your head.

1. 45 + 52 = ... ☐

2. 56 + 27 = ... ☐

3. What number do I add to 38 to make 56? .... ☐

4. Explain how you would add 19 to 67.

_____

_____

5. 65 − 42 = ... ☐

6. 43 − 27 = ... ☐

7. How do I know that 94 − 21 could not be 74?

_____

_____

8. A pair of numbers has a difference of 15. What could those numbers be?

_____

_____

How easy?

Red

Amber

Green

How do you think you have done?

_____

_____

Name			Date		

Products game

You need a set of 1–9 digit cards.

- In pairs, take it in turns to pick a card.
- Multiply the number by 8 or 9. Use a counter to cover the product on the grid below.
- The winner is the first player with a line of four counters.

32	72	80	18	24	8
81	16	48	40	27	45
24	90	63	36	54	64
54	64	24	72	81	56
18	27	36	45	16	72
56	40	32	63	80	27
27	48	16	8	90	64

I know my 8- and 9-times tables. I can use the multiplication facts I know to work out division facts.

How easy?

Red
Amber
Green

How do you think you have done?
_____
_____

BLOCK A

Name	Date

Multiplication and division pairs

1. Choose a number from each box. Multiply your numbers together. Use the grid method.

34	76
79	58

6	5
4	3

×			

2. Now choose a number from each box to create a division.

_____

_____

÷			

◼ Do you have any remainders?

_____

◼ What would your answer be if you rounded it up/down?

_____

How easy?

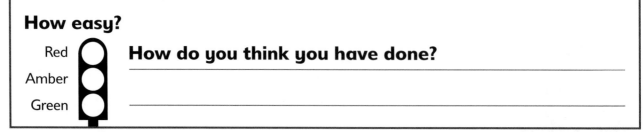

Red
Amber
Green

How do you think you have done?

_____

_____

BLOCK B
Securing number facts, understanding shape

Expected prior learning
Check that children can already:
- recall addition and subtraction facts for each number to 20
- recall multiplication and division facts for the 2-, 3-, 4-, 5-, 6- and 10-times tables
- say a subtraction fact that is the inverse of an addition fact, and a multiplication fact that is the inverse of a division fact, and vice versa
- identify the calculation needed to solve a one-step problem
- name common 2D and 3D shapes, and recognise a 3D shape from a 2D drawing of it
- draw a line of symmetry in a 2D shape
- choose their own criterion for sorting a set of shapes.

Objectives overview
The text in this diagram identifies the focus of mathematics learning within the block.

Key aspects of learning
- Reasoning
- Creative thinking

Patterns, relationships and properties of numbers and shapes

Solving one- and two-step word problems involving numbers, money or measures

Explaining methods and reasoning, orally and on paper, using words, diagrams and symbols

**BLOCK B:
Securing number facts, understanding shape**

Sums and differences of multiples of 10, 100, 100

Tables to 10 × 10; multiples

Doubles of two-digit numbers and multiples of 10, 100; corresponding halves

Properties of polygons, including line symmetry

Visualising 3D and 2D shapes

Nets of common solids

Using a calculator

Unit 1 🔲 Securing number facts, understanding shape

Introduction
In this unit children estimate and check calculations, continue to recall all multiplication facts to 10 × 10, investigate number patterns and relationships, develop their skills in addition and subtraction, and solve word problems. They develop their understanding of the properties of polygons, visualise 3D shapes and draw their nets, and investigate the properties of shapes. Children work in pairs for much of this work, so that they have further opportunities to develop their arguments and to practise ways of presenting them.

Framework objectives	Assessment focuses		Success criteria for Year 4	Learning outcomes
	Level 4	Level 3		
① Using rounding to estimate and check answers				
Use knowledge of rounding, number operations and inverses to estimate and check calculations	• use inverse operations, e.g. • use a calculator and inverse operations to find missing numbers • check the reasonableness of results with reference to the context or size of numbers	• solve whole number problems including those involving multiplication or division that may give rise to remainders, e.g. • identify appropriate operations to use • round up or down after simple division, depending on context	• can round numbers in a calculation to estimate the answer to the calculation	*I can round numbers in a calculation to help me estimate the answer to the calculation.*
② Patterns in equations				
Use knowledge of addition and subtraction facts and place value to derive sums and differences of pairs of multiples of 10, 100 or 1000	• use a range of mental methods of computation with addition and subtraction	• add and subtract two-digit numbers mentally	• can use knowledge of addition and subtraction facts and place value to work out sums and differences of pairs of multiples of 10, 100 and 1000	*Because I know sums like 3 + 7 = 10, I also know 30 + 70 = 100 300 + 700 = 1000 3000 + 7000 = 10,000. Because I know differences like 6 − 4 = 2, I also know 60 − 40 = 20 600 − 400 = 200 6000 − 4000 = 2000.*
Identify and use patterns, relationships and properties of numbers or shapes; investigate a statement involving numbers and test it with examples	• search for a solution by trying out ideas of their own, e.g. • identify patterns as they work and form their own generalisations/rules in words	• understand a general statement by finding particular examples that match it, e.g. • make a generalisation with the assistance of probing questions and prompts	• can identify the patterns that help to add and subtract multiples of 10, 100 and 1000 • can make a general statement and find examples that match it	*I can use what I know about polygons to group them into regular and irregular polygons.*

Unit 1 ▢ Securing number facts, understanding shape

Framework objectives	Assessment focuses		Success criteria for Year 4	Learning outcomes
	Level 4	**Level 3**		
③ Multiplication and division facts				
Derive and recall multiplication facts up to 10 × 10, the corresponding division facts and multiples of numbers to 10 up to the tenth multiple	• quickly derive division facts that correspond to multiplication facts up to 10 × 10 • recall multiplication facts up to 10 × 10 and quickly derive corresponding division facts	• derive associated division facts from known multiplication facts, e.g. ○ given a number sentence, use understanding of operations to create related sentences • use mental recall of the 2, 3, 4, 5 and 10 multiplication tables	• can identify multiples of 2, 3, 4, 5 and 6 and begin to use these to derive multiples of 7, 8 and 9 • can work out division facts from corresponding multiplication facts	*I can work out division facts for the 1-, 2-, 3-, 4-, 5- and 6-times tables I can count in 6s from zero to 60.*
④ Solving one-step and two-step problems				
Solve one-step and two-step problems involving numbers, money or measures, including time; choose and carry out appropriate calculations, using calculator methods where appropriate	• develop own strategies for solving problems, e.g. ○ make their own suggestions of ways to tackle a range of problems ○ make connections to previous work ○ pose and answer questions related to a problem ○ check answers and ensure solutions make sense in the context of the problem ○ review their work and approaches • solve problems with or without a calculator ○ solve two-step problems choosing appropriate operations ○ deal with two constraints simultaneously ○ interpret a calculator display of 4.5 as £4.50 in context of money ○ carry out simple calculations involving negative numbers in context • check the reasonableness of results with reference to the context or size of numbers	• try different approaches and find ways of overcoming difficulties that arise when they are solving problems, e.g. ○ check their work and make appropriate corrections, e.g. decide that two numbers less than 100 cannot give a total more than 200 and correct the addition ○ begin to look for patterns in results as they work and use them to find other possible outcomes • use mental recall of addition and subtraction facts to 20 in solving problems involving larger numbers, e.g. ○ choose to calculate mentally, on paper or with apparatus ○ solve one-step whole number problems appropriately ○ solve two-step problems that involve addition and subtraction	• can solve one- and two-step money problems by choosing appropriate operations • can check answers either without or with a calculator	*I can work out how to solve problems with one or two steps. I can decide what calculation to work out and whether a calculator will help me. I can think about the numbers in a calculation and choose a good way to do the calculation.*

BLOCK B

Unit 1 Securing number facts, understanding shape

Framework objectives	Assessment focuses		Success criteria for Year 4	Learning outcomes
	Level 4	Level 3		
⑤ Making 3D shapes from nets				
Visualise 3D objects from 2D drawings; make nets of common solids	• use the properties of 3D shapes, e.g. • visualise shapes and recognise them in different orientations • make 3D models by linking given faces or edges	• classify 3D shapes, e.g. • recognise common 3D shapes, e.g. triangular prism, square-based pyramid • relate 3D shapes to drawings and photographs of them, including from different viewpoints • begin to recognise nets of familiar 3D shapes, e.g. cube, cuboid, triangular prism, square-based pyramid	• can visualise 3D shapes from 2D pictures of them • can make nets of 3D shapes	*If I see a drawing of a cube or a pyramid I can visualise the solid shapes. I can make a net for an open cube and fold it to check that it is correct.*
⑥ Guess the 2D shape				
Draw polygons and classify them by identifying their properties, including their line symmetry	• use the properties of 2D shapes, e.g. • recognise right-angled, equilateral, isosceles and scalene triangles • recognise an oblique line of symmetry in a shape • understand properties of shapes, e.g. why a square is a special rectangle	• classify 2D shapes in various ways using mathematical properties such as reflective symmetry, e.g. • sort objects and shapes using more than one criterion, e.g. pentagon, not pentagon and all edges the same length/not the same length • sort the shapes which have all edges the same length and all angles the same size from a set of mixed shapes and begin to understand the terms 'regular' and 'irregular' • recognise right angles in shapes in different orientations • recognise angles which are bigger/smaller than 90° and begin to know the terms 'obtuse' and 'acute' • recognise right-angled and equilateral triangles • demonstrate that a shape has reflection symmetry by folding and recognise when a shape does not have a line of symmetry	• can pick out regular and irregular polygons • knows facts about regular polygons such as number of sides, angles and lines of symmetry • can draw a range of polygons	*I know facts about regular polygons such as the number of sides and number of angles. I can pick out irregular polygons that have at least one right angle.*
⑦ Classifying polygons				
Report solutions to puzzles and problems, giving explanations and reasoning orally and in writing, using diagrams and symbols	• present information and results in a clear and organised way, e.g. • organise written work, e.g. record results in order • begin to work in an organised way from the start • consider appropriate units • use related vocabulary accurately	• discuss their mathematical work and begin to explain their thinking, e.g. • use appropriate mathematical vocabulary • talk about their findings by referring to their written work • use and interpret mathematical symbols and diagrams	• can use appropriate mathematical vocabulary to report solutions to problems • can give explanations orally and in writing, using diagrams and symbols	*I can explain to the class how I solved a problem. I can draw a diagram to show how I solved a problem.*

BLOCK B

SCHOLASTIC

Activity ①

Prior learning
Children can round a number to the nearest 10. They can recall addition and subtraction facts to 20.

Framework objective
Use knowledge of rounding, number operations and inverses to estimate and check calculations

Vocabulary
round, estimate, answer, method, explain, rule, add, subtract, sum, total, plus, minus, difference

Resources
Worksheet: Using rounding to estimate and check answers
Resource sheet: 0-9 digit cards
Classroom resources: whiteboards and pens

① Using rounding to estimate and check answers

Tell the children they are going to estimate and check answers to addition and subtraction problems by rounding. Write on the board: 32 + 49. Then write these numbers on the board: 60, 70, 80, 90, 100. Ask the children to show on their whiteboards which of these numbers is about the same as the answer to the addition. *How did you work this out?* Repeat for subtraction, using 52 − 27 and the numbers 10, 20, 30, 40. Provide 0-9 digit cards, and ask the children to complete the worksheet 'Using rounding to estimate and check answers'.

Teacher support
Less confident learners: Let these children work as a group with an adult to assist them. Encourage them to explain how they will round their two-digit numbers.
More confident learners: Challenge these children to make a three-digit number and a two-digit number each time, so that they round, add and subtract two-digit numbers and three-digit numbers (for example, 168 − 37).

Common misconceptions
Children round 32 + 49 to 30 + 40 and estimate the answer 70 because they only look at the tens digits.
Remind children to check the units digit before deciding whether to round up or down. Establish that the estimate for 32 + 49 should be 30 + 50 with an estimated answer of 80.

Children round down from a two-digit number ending in 5 rather than up.
Clarify by asking a child the rule and providing more practice of rounding two-digit numbers.

Probing questions
● What is the rule for rounding numbers?
● How did you round these numbers? What did you do to check your answers?

Next steps
Support: Provide further experience of rounding numbers and number sentences, until the children are secure with rounding. See also Year 4 Block A Unit 1.
Extension: Using three- or four-digit numbers, ask the children to complete the same task but rounding to the nearest 100 or 1000. See also Year 5 Block B Unit 1.

Activity ②

Prior learning
Children can recall addition and subtraction facts for each number to 20.

Framework objectives
- Identify and use patterns, relationships and properties of numbers or shapes; investigate a statement involving numbers and test it with examples
- Use knowledge of addition and subtraction facts and place value to derive sums and differences of pairs of multiples of 10, 100 or 1000

Vocabulary
problem, solution, equation, calculate, operation, inverse, answer, method, pattern, relationship, rule, add, subtract, sum, total, difference, plus, minus, multiple

Resources
Display page: Patterns in equations
Resource sheets: Self-assessment, Place value arrow cards

② Patterns in equations

Reveal the display page 'Patterns in equations'. Ask the children to identify and explain the patterns and relationships between the equations. Invite them to explain to a partner how the first equation can help them to work out the others. Now ask them to use what they have learned and to work in pairs or groups to devise ten questions and answers. Pairs or groups can then challenge the rest of the class to derive answers to their questions. Decide whether to use the self-assessment sheet for the children to record their achievements and what they need to do next.

Teacher support
Less confident learners: With an adult or more confident learner, ask these children to compare the addition and subtraction of numbers to 10 with addition and subtraction of multiples of 10 and discuss what the children observe. Use place value arrow cards to illustrate. For example: 6 + 3 = 9; 60 + 30 = 90.
More confident learners: Ask these children to show and explain their own examples to less confident learners and work out new examples together. They could use place value cards to illustrate what is happening.

Common misconception
Children do not recognise the relationship between addition and subtraction of single-digit numbers and addition and subtraction of multiples of 10, 100 and 1000.
Provide more practice using place value arrow cards. Provide support in writing number sentences such as: I know that 2 + 3 = 5, so I can work out that 20 + 30 = 50. I know that 5 − 3 = 2, so I can work out that 50 − 30 = 20.

Probing questions
- What do you notice about the equation 11 + 5 = 16? What is 1100 + 500? And 1600 − 500?
- How do you know that this is the correct answer?

Next steps
Support: Provide further experience of multiplying by 10, 100 and 1000 and working out equations involving numbers to 10 and then their multiples of 10 and 100. See also Year 3 Block B.
Extension: Ask the children to make up and solve word problems that involve adding or subtracting multiples of 10, 100 or 1000. For example: *There are 160 pears in the crate. 70 are sold. How many are left?* See also Year 5 Block B.

Activity ③

Prior learning
Children can recall multiplication and division facts for the 2-, 3-, 4-, 5-, 6- and 10-times tables.

Framework objective
Derive and recall multiplication facts up to 10 × 10, the corresponding division facts and multiples of numbers to 10 up to the tenth multiple

Vocabulary
operation, inverse, answer, method, explain, relationship, rule, multiply, divide, product, factor, multiple, divisor

Resources
Resource sheets: 100-square, Self-assessment
Classroom resources: counters, squared paper

③ Multiplication and division facts

Write on the board the multiplication sentence 8 × 9. Say: *Write as many ways as you can of working out the answer.* Provide a copy of the resource sheet '100-square' for each child and ask them to colour round the numbers in the 6-, 7-, 8- and 9-times tables (each table in a different colour). Ask them to list the ways that the 100-square and the colours can help them to recall multiplication and division facts. Decide whether to use the self-assessment sheet for the children to record their achievements and next steps.

Teacher support
Less confident learners: Show the children a 100-square and identify the pattern of 3s and 6s. *How does the 3-times table help you with the 6-times table? How can doubling and halving help? How can the colours on the 100-square help you to work out division facts? Show me how you can work out 30 divided by 6.*
More confident learners: Ask these children to draw rectangles on squared paper to show multiplication facts and their corresponding division facts. For example, the rectangle below could be used to show: 6 × 4 = 24; 4 × 6 = 24; 24 ÷ 6 = 4; 24 ÷ 4 = 6.

Common misconceptions
Children do not remember the commutative law for multiplication, which would help to recall other multiplication facts (for example, 3 × 6 = 6 × 3).
Use a multiplication square to investigate this further.

Children think that the commutative law applies to division (for example, they think that 18 ÷ 3 = 3 ÷ 18).
Put out 18 counters and ask children to group them in sets of 3. Write 18 ÷ 3 = 6. Write 3 ÷ 18, and put out 3 counters. Ask children if they can group 3 into sets of 18. (No.) This shows that 3 ÷ 18 is not the same as 18 ÷ 3.

Probing questions
● I think of a number, multiply it by 6 and the answer is 54. What is the number?
● If you know 6 × 7 = 42, what division facts do you also know?

Next steps

Support: Let the children repeat the 100-square activity to find other multiplication facts (for example, in the 2-, 5- and 7-times tables). See also Year 4 Block A Unit 1.

Extension: Ask the children to investigate, using rectangles on squared paper, multiplication and division facts for multiples of 10. For example, if they know $6 \times 4 = 24$, how can this help them to find 60×4? See also Year 4 Block E Unit 2.

BLOCK B

Activity ④

Prior learning

Children can identify the calculation needed to solve a one-step problem. Where appropriate, they can use a calculator to solve word problems. They can compare solutions with others' and identify the best approaches. They are able to make decisions about the number sentences they can draw upon to represent a problem.

Framework objective

Solve one-step and two-step problems involving numbers, money or measures, including time; choose and carry out appropriate calculations, using calculator methods where appropriate

Vocabulary

problem, solution, calculator, calculate, calculation, equation, operation, inverse, answer, method, explain, predict, reason, add, subtract, sum, total, difference, plus, minus

Resources

Display page: Solving one-step and two-step problems
Worksheets: Solving one-step and two-step problems (1) and (2)

④ Solving one-step and two-step problems

Reveal the display page 'Solving one-step and two-step problems'. Together with the children, go through the steps required to solve the different problems featured on the screen.

Teacher support

Less confident learners: Provide the worksheet 'Solving one-step and two-step problems (1)'. Ask the children to work with an adult to complete it.
More confident learners: Provide the worksheet 'Solving one-step and two-step problems (2)'. Invite the children to check their answers in pairs and talk about what operations they carried out to get all their answers. Ask each pair to write down number sentences to show their calculations. They may also use a calculator to do a final check.

Common misconception

Children confuse which number operation to use for each part of a word problem.
Encourage discussion as to how to convert a word problem into a number sentence. Ask whether answers are realistic. Ensure that the children check answers by using an inverse operation when appropriate.

Probing questions
● How did you know that you had to use addition for this part? What words in the question showed you this?
● How did you calculate how much Dad has left after his three goes on the 'Win a teddy' game and his drink?

Next steps
Support: Ask these children to work with an adult and a partner to devise word problems from simple number sentences. For example, for £2 − £0.99: *I went to the shop with £2 and bought a toy for 99p. How much change did I get?* Work also with measures. See also Year 3 Block B.
Extension: Ask the children to devise word problems referring to measures, including time. They should work in pairs and derive appropriate number sentences. They can check their answers with a calculator and report back to others. See also Year 4 Block B Units 2 and 3.

Activity ⑤

Prior learning
Children can name common 2D and 3D shapes and recognise a 3D shape from a 2D drawing of it.

Framework objective
Visualise 3D objects from 2D drawings; make nets of common solids

Vocabulary
3D, three-dimensional, 2D, two-dimensional, net, construct, regular, irregular, vertex, vertices, face, edge, polygon, equilateral triangle, isosceles triangle, quadrilateral, rectangle, square, oblong, hexagon, heptagon, octagon

Resources
Resource sheet: Self-assessment
Classroom resources: paper, rulers, pencils, plastic or wooden 2D and 3D shapes, scissors, selection of nets

⑤ Making 3D shapes from nets

Ask the children to work in pairs and describe to each other the properties of a cube. Ask one child in each pair to draw the net as their partner describes it. Ask: *Can you cut out the net and make the solid shape?* Decide whether to use the self-assessment sheet for the children to record their achievements and what they need to do next.

Teacher support
Less confident learners: Ask these children to work in a small group with an adult who can draw the net as the group describes what to draw. If necessary, use a 3D cube for reference and ask the children to describe what they see before asking them to describe it from memory.
More confident learners: When pairs have finished working on the cube, ask them to describe and draw the net of a cuboid, and construct the cuboid from the net. They can then compare the properties of a cube and a cuboid.

Common misconceptions
Children do not use the correct mathematical vocabulary (for example, vertices, edges, faces).
Provide plenty of opportunities for children to describe 3D shapes using this vocabulary through 'guess the shape' type games.

Children confuse cubes and cuboids.
Allow more practice in comparing 3D shapes and drawing their nets.

BLOCK B

Probing questions
- What is the difference between the net of a cube and the net of a cylinder?
- How many faces, edges and vertices does each shape have?
- What are the faces called?

Next steps
Support: Provide nets of a cuboid and nets of other types of prism. Discuss what is the same and what is different. Ask the children to construct the shapes from the nets they have. Let them work in a group with an adult if possible. See also Year 4 Block B Unit 1.
Extension: Ask the children to make a net of an open cube and construct the 3D shape. See also Year 4 Block B Unit 3.

Activity ⑥

Prior learning
Children can identify and draw lines of symmetry in a 2D shape. They are able to choose their own criteria for sorting a set of shapes.

Framework objective
Draw polygons and classify them by identifying their properties, including their line symmetry

Vocabulary
symmetrical, line of symmetry, polygon, equilateral triangle, isosceles triangle, quadrilateral, rectangle, square, oblong, hexagon, heptagon, octagon, regular, irregular

Resources
Resource sheet: Self-assessment
Classroom resources: range of 2D shapes, squared paper, rulers, pencils

⑥ Guess the 2D shape

Ask children to work in pairs to write descriptions of 2D shapes and draw them. Invite pairs to describe the shapes to the rest of the class, who should identify them either by name or by matching with prepared shapes. Decide whether to use the self-assessment sheet to record achievements and next steps.

Teacher support
Less confident learners: Let groups work with an adult and/or provide a prompt sheet with relevant vocabulary. Provide plastic 2D shapes as support.
More confident learners: Ask children to write descriptions of irregular shapes. Give target vocabulary and ask them to work in pairs to guess each shape.

Common misconception
Children think that all polygons are regular shapes.
Practise describing and drawing irregular polygons.

Probing questions
- How many shapes can you draw that have at least one right angle?
- What is another name for a rectangle? Describe its properties.

Next steps
Support: Encourage the children to use a variety of equipment (for example, geostrips and ICT programs) to make and draw triangles, quadrilaterals, pentagons, hexagons, heptagons and octagons. See also Year 3 Block B.
Extension: Ask the children to use a variety of practical equipment and/or ICT programs to make regular and irregular triangles, quadrilaterals, pentagons, hexagons, heptagons and octagons. See also Year 4 Block B Units 2 and 3.

Activity ⑦

Prior learning
Children can choose their own criteria for sorting a set of shapes. They can use correct mathematical vocabulary to describe a range of polygons and their properties, including line symmetry.

Framework objective
Report solutions to puzzles and problems, giving explanations and reasoning orally and in writing, using diagrams and symbols

Vocabulary
problem, solution, explain, sort, classify, Carroll diagram, 2D, symmetrical, line of symmetry, polygon, equilateral triangle, isosceles triangle, quadrilateral, rectangle, square, oblong, hexagon, heptagon, octagon, regular, irregular

Resources
Display page: Classifying polygons
Resource sheets: Classifying polygons, Carroll diagram, Self-assessment
Classroom resources: glue, scissors, isometric paper

⑦ Classifying polygons

Provide each child with the resource sheets 'Classifying polygons' and 'Carroll diagram'. Reveal the display page 'Classifying polygons'. Invite the children to decide what criteria they could use on the Carroll diagram (for example, irregular, regular, four sides or fewer). Ask them to cut out the shapes on the worksheet and stick them into the appropriate parts of the Carroll diagram. Invite them to report to a partner how and why they sorted their shapes in the way they have done. They should then write down any alternative ways the shapes could have been sorted. Decide whether to use the self-assessment sheet for the children to record their achievements and next steps.

Teacher support
Less confident learners: Let these children work as a group with an adult and discuss possible criteria. Ensure that they can name all the polygons and are able to recognise whether they are regular or irregular and whether they have lines of symmetry.
More confident learners: Encourage these children to listen to other pairs who have written explanations and solutions and completed diagrams. They should make notes on what they say in order to report back to the class.

Common misconception
Children do not understand mathematical vocabulary correctly. For example, they think that a quadrilateral is a shape with four right angles, or that all triangles are regular polygons.
Ask children to look at and then draw a range of four-sided polygons without right angles. Remind them of the definition of a regular polygon.

Probing questions
- Why did you choose those criteria?
- How did you know where to place the shape in the Carroll diagram?
- Tell me another shape that could go into this position. How do you know?

Next steps
Support: Encourage these children to draw shapes on isometric paper, with adult support, and to investigate and report on the shapes' properties. See also Year 3 Block B Unit 1.
Extension: Invite these children to use isometric or squared paper to draw and investigate combining two shapes, and to to report findings. Also refer to Year 4 Block B Unit 2.

Unit 2 ▢ Securing number facts, understanding shape

Introduction
In this unit the children find patterns, relationships and properties of numbers and shapes, explaining methods and reasoning, orally and on paper, using words, diagrams and symbols. They explore using a calculator and continue to find sums and differences of multiples of 10, 100 and 1000, using tables to 10 × 10. They investigate doubles of two-digit numbers, and multiples of 10 and 100, and their corresponding halves. Children develop their knowledge of properties of polygons, including line symmetry, visualising 3D and 2D shapes, and finding nets of common solids.

Framework objectives	Assessment focuses		Success criteria for Year 4	Learning outcomes
	Level 4	Level 3		
① Using inverses to check calculations				
Use knowledge of rounding, number operations and inverses to estimate and check calculations	• use inverse operations, e.g. • use a calculator and inverse operations to find missing numbers • check the reasonableness of results with reference to the context or size of numbers	• solve whole-number problems, including those involving multiplication or division that may give rise to remainders, e.g. • identify appropriate operations to use • round up or down after simple division, depending on context	• can use inverses to check calculations either with or without a calculator • can recognise subtraction as the inverse of addition and can recognise division as the inverse of multiplication	*If I add two numbers I can use subtraction to check whether my answer is correct* *If I divide one number by another I can use multiplication to check whether my answer is correct*
② Patterns and relationships between numbers				
Identify and use patterns, relationships and properties of numbers or shapes; investigate a statement involving numbers and test it with examples	• search for a solution by trying out ideas of their own, e.g. • identify patterns as they work and form their own generalisations/rules in words	• understand a general statement by finding particular examples that match it, e.g. • make a generalisation with the assistance of probing questions and prompts	• can see number patterns in the answers to tables • can see number patterns in the 100-square and on number lines that can help them form their own generalisations and rules	*I can see number patterns in the answers to the 3-times table and can explain how the pattern works* *I can spot a rule about the number of lines of symmetry that regular polygons have*

Unit 2 ☐ Securing number facts, understanding shape

Framework objectives	Assessment focuses		Success criteria for Year 4	Learning outcomes
	Level 4	Level 3		
③ **Finding answers by doubling or halving** ④ **Doubling and halving**				
Identify the doubles of two-digit numbers; use these to calculate doubles of multiples of 10 and 100 and derive the corresponding halves	● recognise and describe number relationships ● use inverse operations	● add and subtract two-digit numbers mentally ● use mental recall of the 2 multiplication table	● can identify the doubles and halves of two-digit numbers and can use these to work out the doubles and halves of multiples of 10 and 100	*Because I know that double 7 is 14, I know that double 70 is 140.* *I can work out doubles of numbers with two digits.*
③ **Finding answers by doubling or halving** ④ **Doubling and halving** ⑦ **Explain yourselves!** ⑧ **Division facts**				
Derive and recall multiplication facts up to 10 × 10, the corresponding division facts and multiples of numbers to 10 up to the tenth multiple	● quickly derive division facts that correspond to multiplication facts up to 10 × 10 ● recall multiplication facts up to 10 × 10 and quickly derive corresponding division facts	● derive associated division facts from known multiplication facts, e.g. ● given a number sentence, use understanding of operations to create related sentences ● use mental recall of the 2, 3, 4, 5 and 10 multiplication tables	● can use knowledge of known tables to begin to learn less familiar tables ● can use known multiplication facts to derive associated division facts	*I can tell you answers to the 8-times table, even when the questions are not in order.*
⑤ **Name the 3D shape**				
Visualise 3D objects from 2D drawings; make nets of common solids	● use the properties of 3D shapes, e.g. ● visualise shapes and recognise them in different orientations ● make 3D models by linking given faces or edges	● classify 3D shapes, e.g. ● recognise common 3D shapes, e.g. triangular prism, square-based pyramid ● relate 3D shapes to drawings and photographs of them, including from different viewpoints ● begin to recognise nets of familiar 3D shapes, e.g. cube, cuboid, triangular prism, square-based pyramid	● can visualise and name a shape from 2D drawings ● can describe the properties of 3D shapes ● can construct a 3D shape from straws	*If I see a drawing of a cube I can imagine the solid shape* *I can make different nets for cubes and fold them to check they are correct.*

Unit 2 ☐ Securing number facts, understanding shape

BLOCK B

Framework objectives	Assessment focuses		Success criteria for Year 4	Learning outcomes
	Level 4	Level 3		
⑥ Constructing polygons				
Draw polygons and classify them by identifying their properties, including their line symmetry	● use the properties of 2D shapes, e.g. ● recognise right-angled, equilateral, isosceles and scalene triangles ● recognise an oblique line of symmetry in a shape ● understand properties of shapes, e.g. why a square is a special rectangle	● classify 2D shapes in various ways using mathematical properties such as reflective symmetry, e.g. ● sort objects and shapes using more than one criterion, e.g. pentagon, not pentagon and all edges the same length/not the same length ● sort the shapes which have all edges the same length and all angles the same size from a set of mixed shapes and begin to understand the terms 'regular' and 'irregular' ● recognise right angles in shapes in different orientations ● recognise angles which are bigger/smaller than 90° and begin to know the terms 'obtuse' and 'acute' ● recognise right-angled and equilateral triangles ● demonstrate that a shape has reflection symmetry by folding and recognise when a shape does not have a line of symmetry	● can construct and name a range of polygons ● can recognise the properties of a range of regular and irregular polygons	*I can use what I know about triangles to group them into equilateral triangles, isosceles triangles and other triangles. I can pick out triangles that have a right angle from other triangles. I can recognise symmetrical polygons, including those with more than one line of symmetry.*
⑦ Explain yourselves!				
Report solutions to puzzles and problems, giving explanations and reasoning orally and in writing, using diagrams and symbols	● present information and results in a clear and organised way, e.g. ● organise written work, e.g. record results in order ● begin to work in an organised way from the start ● consider appropriate units ● use related vocabulary accurately	● discuss their mathematical work and begin to explain their thinking, e.g. ● use appropriate mathematical vocabulary ● talk about their findings by referring to their written work ● use and interpret mathematical symbols and diagrams	● can discuss mathematical work ● can write an explanation of how to solve a problem which includes number sentences involving all number operations ● can talk about findings by referring to written work	*I can write an explanation of how I solved a problem.* *I can include number sentences using the +, -, × or ÷ signs where I need to.*

📖SCHOLASTIC

Activity ①

Prior learning

Children can recall addition and subtraction facts for each number to 20. They can say a subtraction fact that is the inverse of an addition fact.

Framework objective

Use knowledge of rounding, number operations and inverses to estimate and check calculations

Vocabulary

check, calculation, equation, operation, inverse, answer, method, explain, relationship, rule, add, subtract, sum, total, difference, plus, minus

Resources

Interactive activity: Function machine
Resource sheet: Self-assessment
Classroom resources: counting items, whiteboards and pens

① Using inverses to check calculations

Open the interactive activity 'Function machine'. Enter 48 in the left-hand window and −27 in the middle window. Click 'Go'. Before revealing the answer in the right-hand window, ask the children to write the calculation as a number sentence on their whiteboards: 48 − 27 = 21. Ask them to use an inverse operation to check the calculation on the function machine: 21 + 27 = 48 or 27 + 21 = 48. Invite them to suggest other two-digit numbers and operations for the left-hand and middle windows and repeat. Decide whether to use the self-assessment sheet for the children to record their achievements and what they need to do next.

Teacher support

Less confident learners: Ask these children to work as a group with an adult to clarify inverse operations with numbers below 20; for example, ask them to use inverse operations to check 14 + 2, 17 − 8.
More confident learners: Encourage these children to explain how to check multiplication and division calculations using inverse operations. Ask them to write their own examples.

Common misconception

Children do not recognise that addition and subtraction are inverse operations. Use sets of counters, cubes or other objects to demonstrate that addition 'undoes' subtraction and vice versa. For example: *I have 13 counters. I take 5 away and I have 8 left. 13 take away 5 is 8. I add 5 and I have 13 counters. 8 add 5 is 13.*

Probing questions

● What is the inverse operation that you can use to check this answer?
● How could you use inverse operations to help you to check the answer to 76 − 48?

Next steps

Support: Give these children a set of addition calculations and ask them to write the subtractions that they could use to check them. Repeat for checking subtraction with addition. See also Year 3 Block B Unit 3.
Extension: Ask the children to devise word problems that involve calculations that can be checked using inverse operations. They could work with a partner or in a group. See also Year 4 Block B Unit 3.

BLOCK B

Activity ②

BLOCK B

Prior learning
Children can count forwards and backwards in steps of different sizes. They recall multiplication and division facts for the 2-, 3-, 4-, 5-, 6- and 10-times tables.

Framework objective
Identify and use patterns, relationships and properties of numbers or shapes; investigate a statement involving numbers and test it with examples

Vocabulary
units, tens, multiples, pattern, sequence, add, subtract, sum, total, difference, plus, minus

Resources
Worksheet: Patterns and relationships between numbers
Resource sheets: 100-square, Blank number lines

② Patterns and relationships between numbers

Start with oral activities: *Join in with this sequence when you recognise it: 4, 8, 12, … Who can complete this number sequence? 40, 36, 32, 28, 24, 20, …* Ask the children to complete the worksheet 'Patterns and relationships between numbers'.

Teacher support
Less confident learners: Provide children with copies of the 100-square. Ask them to colour patterns of 2, 3, 5, 10 and so on. Encourage them then to practise saying their sequences aloud to a partner, from memory if possible.
More confident learners: Suggest that these children devise their own sequences and ask their partner: *What is the rule?* They could record and report their ideas to the rest of the class.

Common misconceptions
Children think that there are no numbers below zero.
Practise counting below zero, emphasising minus numbers. Use a number line where 0 is in the middle.

Children think that numbers beyond 100 or 1000 don't increase in steps of 1.
Make the starting point of a count 90 and the finishing point 120. Make the starting point 990 and the finishing point 1020. Count on and back in ones each time.

Probing questions
● What can we do when we are counting down and want to carry on below zero?
● Can you complete a 100-square that begins at 100 and ends at 199? Would 43 be on it? Would 143?

Next steps
Support: Provide a blank number line and discuss with children what sequences they can generate. Share ideas in the group. Each child writes a different sequence on their number line and explains the rule. See also Year 4 Block A Unit 1.
Extension: Children can work independently or in groups to generate sequences on number lines, which involve both plus and minus numbers. They should place 0 in the centre of a blank number line and decide on a rule. They could leave some parts blank and challenge a partner to complete it. See also Year 4 Block D Unit 1.

Activities ③ and ④

BLOCK B

Prior learning
Children can recall multiplication and division facts for the 2-, 3-, 4-, 5-, 6- and 10-times tables.

Framework objectives
● Identify the doubles of two-digit numbers; use these to calculate doubles of multiples of 10 and 100 and derive the corresponding halves
● **Derive and recall multiplication facts up to 10 × 10, the corresponding division facts and multiples of numbers to 10 up to the tenth multiple**

Vocabulary
double, halve, multiply, divide, operation, inverse, answer, method, explain, relationship, rule

Resources
Worksheets: Finding answers by doubling or halving, Doubling and halving

③ Finding answers by doubling or halving

Write a multiplication from the 8-times table on the board (for example, 4 × 8). *How can knowing doubles or halves and knowing the 4-times table help you work out the answer?* Ask the children to give some examples of their own. Provide the worksheet 'Finding answers by doubling or halving' and ask the children to answer the questions. When they have finished, ask: *If you can divide 15 by 3 can you divide 150 by 3? And 300 by 6?*

Teacher support
Less confident learners: Let these children work with an adult in small groups. Ensure that they understand the relationships that have been discussed. For example: *30 ÷ 3 = 10 so 15 ÷ 3 = 5. How do we know this?*
More confident learners: Ask these children to use their knowledge of doubling and halving to give examples of finding the corresponding doubles and halves of multiples of 10 and 100. For example: *I know that double 9 is 18 so I know that double 90 is 180 and that double 900 is 1800. I know that half of 18 is 9 so I know that half of 180 is 90 and that half of 1800 is 900.*

Common misconceptions
Children lack secure knowledge of halves and doubles.
Practise identifying doubles and halves of numbers to 20 and their multiples of 10 and 100.

Children lack secure knowledge of times tables.
Encourage children to practise times-table facts by completing tables squares. Discuss their answers and help them to notice what they already know and how these facts can help them learn new ones.

Probing questions
● Identify multiples of 4 and 8 on a 100-square. What do you notice?
● Identify multiples of 3 and 6 on another 100-square. What do you notice?

Next steps
Support: Simplify the examples the children are working with. See also Year 4 Block B Unit 1.
Extension: Ask these children to work with multiples of 10 and 100 to derive similar examples. See also Year 4 Block B Unit 3.

④ Doubling and halving

Ask the children how doubling relates to both addition and multiplication. *How can you represent 70 + 70 as a multiplication?* (70 × 2) *How could you work out double 16?* For example, (10 × 2) + (6 × 2) = 20 + 12 = 32. *How could you halve 32?* For example, (30 ÷ 2) + (2 ÷ 2) = 15 + 1 = 16. Listen for strategies such as 'double the tens, double the units, and add them together', 'halve the tens, halve the units and add the answers together'. Hand out copies of the worksheet 'Doubling and halving' for the children to complete.

Teacher support
Less confident learners: Help these children to think of more examples. Encourage them to write questions to help understand the strategy.
More confident learners: Ask the children to write strategies for doubling and halving three-digit numbers. Get them to make up some questions of their own.

Common misconception
Children do not appreciate that dividing by 2 and halving are equivalent. Provide practice in splitting groups of objects in half to demonstrate that dividing by 2 and halving give the same result. Use a variety of mathematical vocabulary as you do so, such as: *Let's halve the number in the group. Divide the objects into two groups. What is 16 divided by 2? What is half of 16?*

Probing questions
● What is double 76? How do you know?
● What is half of 138? How do you know?

Next steps
Support: Ask an adult to work with a small group, or a more confident child could be paired with a less confident partner. See also Year 4 Block A Unit 1.
Extension: Ask these children to explain the relationship between doubling and halving. See also Year 4 Block B Unit 3.

Activity ⑤

Prior learning Children can name common 3D shapes.	**Framework objective** Visualise 3D objects from 2D drawings; make nets of common solids
	Vocabulary 3D, three-dimensional, 2D, two-dimensional, vertex, vertices, face, edge
	Resources **Display page:** Name the 3D shape **Worksheet:** Name the 3D shape **Classroom resources:** art straws, scissors

⑤ Name the 3D shape

Give the children the worksheet 'Name the 3D shape'. Ask them to look at each 3D shape illustrated on the sheet and to complete the table below by naming the different shapes and describing their properties.

Teacher support
Less confident learners: Display the interactive activity 'Name the 3D shape'. Ask the children to make a cube from straws. *How many straws have we used? How many corners are there? How many faces?*

BLOCK B

Unit 2 Securing number facts, understanding shape

More confident learners: Ask children to construct 3D shapes using straws.

Common misconception
Children have difficulty using the vocabulary of 3D shapes, such as 'vertices', 'edges', 'faces'.
Provide plenty of opportunities to describe 3D shapes, using this vocabulary through 'guess the shape' type games.

Probing questions
● How many straws would you need to construct a cuboid/a cube/a triangular prism?
● Would all the straws have to be the same length for each of these shapes?

Next steps
Support: Provide these children with opportunities for further practice in describing 3D shapes. See also Year 4 Block B Unit 1.
Extension: Ask the children to explain how the nets of two 3D shapes differ from one another. For example: *List the differences between the nets of a cube and a cuboid.* See also Year 4 Block B Unit 3.

Activity ⑥

Prior learning
Children can name common 2D shapes.

Framework objective
Draw polygons and classify them by identifying their properties, including their line symmetry

Vocabulary
symmetrical, line of symmetry, polygon, equilateral, isosceles triangle, quadrilateral, rectangle, square, hexagon, heptagon, octagon, regular, irregular

Resources
Resource sheets: Constructing polygons, Self-assessment
Classroom resources: geo-rods (or drawing tool on interactive whiteboard), mirrors, 2D plastic or paper shapes

⑥ Constructing polygons

Ask pairs of children to construct and name quadrilaterals. Show and describe them to the rest of the class. Ask other children: *Do you know the name of this quadrilateral? Is it a regular or irregular polygon? Does it have any lines of symmetry?* Repeat with triangles, pentagons and hexagons. Decide whether to use the self-assessment sheet for the children to record achievements and next steps.

Teacher support
Less confident learners: Provide the resource sheet 'Constructing polygons' to support these children.
More confident learners: Invite these children to complete a table of results to show what they know about polygons.

Common misconception
Children are unable to identify lines of symmetry.
Provide mirrors and paper shapes for children to fold to investigate line symmetry.

Probing questions
- Name the quadrilaterals that have more than one line of symmetry.
- What do you know about the lines of symmetry of regular polygons?

Next steps
Support: Provide prepared shapes and ask the children to sort them in different ways according to the shapes' properties. See also Year 4 Block B Unit 1.
Extension: Ask children to draw a Carroll diagram, choose their own criteria and place a variety of plastic or paper polygons on it. See also Year 4 Block B Unit 3.

Activity ⑦

Prior learning
Children can recall most multiplication and corresponding division facts up to 10 × 10.

Framework objectives
- **Derive and recall multiplication facts up to 10 × 10, the corresponding division facts and multiples of numbers to 10 up to the tenth multiple**
- Report solutions to puzzles and problems, giving explanations and reasoning orally and in writing, using diagrams and symbols

Resources
Interactive activity: Multiplication square
Resource sheets: Multiplication square, Self-assessment

⑦ Explain yourselves!

Display the interactive activity 'Multiplication square'. Highlight 2 × 3 and 2 × 4 on the grid. Ask: *What is the sum of these two answers?* I highlight the answer to 2 × 7. *What do you notice?* (2 × 3 and 2 × 4 is 6 + 8 = 14; 2 × 7 = 14.) Give each pair of children a copy of the resource sheet 'Multiplication square' and ask them to check whether this is a reliable way to calculate 7-times table facts. Ask each pair to report their findings. Decide whether to use the self-assessment sheet for the children to record their achievements and next steps.

Teacher support
Less confident learners: Ask these children to investigate the link between the 2- and 3-times tables and the 5-times table. Tell them to colour these facts on the resource sheet 'Multiplication square'. Show them how to use an array to illustrate this (for example, 5 columns of 7 can be split into 3 columns of 7 and 2 columns of 7).
More confident learners: Ask these children to find ways of learning the 9-times table by using the same method with their own choice of tables.

Common misconception
Children lack secure knowledge of times tables facts.
Provide plenty of practice at recalling multiplication and division facts by playing games and completing quizzes.

Probing questions
- How many ways did you find of remembering more difficult tables facts? Why did you choose these methods?
- How might diagrams help? Show me how.

Next steps
Support: Make loop cards for multiplication facts and play in a small group. See also similar work in this unit on multiplication.
Extension: Ask children to investigate and report on what happens with larger numbers, such as 16 × 3 = 10 × 3 and 6 × 3. See also Year 4 Block B Unit 3.

Activity ⑧

Prior learning
Children can recall multiplication and division facts for the 2-, 3-, 4-, 5-, 6- and 10-times tables.

Framework objective
Derive and recall multiplication facts up to 10 × 10, the corresponding division facts and multiples of numbers to 10 up to the tenth multiple

Vocabulary
multiply, divide, double, halve, factor, multiple, divisor, quotient

Resources
Interactive activity: Division facts

⑧ Division facts

Show the children the interactive activity 'Division facts'. In this activity they are required to calculate the answers to a range of division questions.

Teacher support
Less confident learners: Before the children start working through the interactive activity, discuss the mathematical vocabulary that is used. Use a paper copy of the questions. Demonstrate the inverse relationship of multiplication and division by using illustrations such as arrays.
More confident learners: Encourage these children to time themselves as they work through the questions and speed up their responses. Encourage them to look for ways of learning the 7-, 8- and 9-times tables and corresponding division facts.

Common misconception
Children think that division is commutative.
Use real-life problems such as: *There are 30 eggs divided into boxes of six. How many boxes will that be?* (5) Point out that if there are only six eggs and 30 boxes there will not be five boxes full of eggs!

Probing questions
● How could you write these questions using symbols rather than words?
● How can you work out a division fact that you don't know by heart?
● What multiplication fact did you use to help you?

Next steps
Support: Let these children work in pairs to devise some quick-fire questions relating to division. Provide multiplication squares to help them acquire faster recall. See also Year 4 Block A Unit 1.
Extension: Encourage these children to devise more quick-fire questions to help acquire instant recall of multiplication and division facts. See also Year 4 Block B Unit 3.

Unit 3 ▢ Securing number facts, understanding shape

Introduction
In this unit, children continue to solve one- and two-step word problems involving numbers, money or measures. They find patterns, relationships and properties of numbers and shapes, explaining methods and reasoning, orally and on paper, using words, diagrams and symbols. They further explore using a calculator to find sums and differences of multiples of 10, 100 and 1000, using tables to 10 × 10 and multiples. They continue to investigate doubles of two-digit numbers and multiples of 10 and 100, and their corresponding halves. Children develop further their knowledge of properties of polygons, including line symmetry, visualising 3D and 2D shapes, and finding nets of common solids.

Framework objectives	Assessment focuses		Success criteria for Year 4	Learning outcomes
	Level 4	Level 3		
① Properties of polygons ② Equation families				
Identify and use patterns, relationships and properties of numbers or shapes; investigate a statement involving numbers and test it with examples	• search for a solution by trying out ideas of their own, e.g. • identify patterns as they work and form their own generalisations/rules in words	• understand a general statement by finding particular examples that match it, e.g. • make a generalisation with the assistance of probing questions and prompts	• can draw polygons on triangular grid paper and classify them according to the properties they have in common • can start with an equation and use knowledge of number patterns to create a family of equations	*I can start with a calculation such as 18 − 3 = 15 and use number patterns to create a family of calculations with the same answer.* *I can draw polygons on grid paper and pick out some of the properties they have in common.*
③ Will you be on time?				
Solve one-step and two-step problems involving numbers, money or measures, including time; choose and carry out appropriate calculations, using calculator methods where appropriate	• develop own strategies for solving problems • solve problems with or without a calculator, e.g. • solve two-step problems choosing appropriate operations • check the reasonableness of results with reference to the context or size of numbers	• try different approaches and find ways of overcoming difficulties that arise when they are solving problems • use mental recall of addition and subtraction facts to 20 in solving problems involving larger numbers	• can decide what number operation to use • can choose a good way to do the calculation	*I can work out how to solve one- or two-step problems.* *I can decide what calculation to work out and whether a calculator will help me.* *I can think about the numbers and choose a good way to do the calculation.*

■ SCHOLASTIC

Unit 3 ▢ Securing number facts, understanding shape

Framework objectives	Assessment focuses		Success criteria for Year 4	Learning outcomes
	Level 4	Level 3		
④ Arrays and inverse operations ⑨ Inverse operations				
Derive and recall multiplication facts up to 10 × 10, the corresponding division facts and multiples of numbers to 10 up to the tenth multiple	● quickly derive division facts that correspond to multiplication facts up to 10 × 10 ● recall multiplication facts up to 10 × 10 and quickly derive corresponding division facts	● derive associated division facts from known multiplication facts, e.g. ● given a number sentence, use understanding of operations to create related sentences ● use mental recall of the 2, 3, 4, 5 and 10 multiplication tables	● can recall an increasing number of multiplication facts ● can quickly derive division facts that correspond to multiplication facts ● knows what a factor of a number is	*I can tell you answers to the 9-times table, even when the questions are not in order. If you give me a multiplication fact I can give you one or two division facts that go with it. I know what a factor means.*
⑤ Report on polygons				
Report solutions to puzzles and problems, giving explanations and reasoning orally and in writing, using diagrams and symbols	● present information and results in a clear and organised way	● discuss their mathematical work and begin to explain their thinking ● use and interpret mathematical symbols and diagrams	● can talk about what they have found out and refer to written work	*I can describe how I solved a problem about shapes using mathematical vocabulary.*

Draw polygons and classify them by identifying their properties, including their line symmetry	● use the properties of 2D shapes, e.g.
	  ● recognise right-angled, equilateral, isosceles and scalene triangles
	  ● recognise an oblique line of symmetry in a shape
	  ● understand properties of shapes, e.g. why a square is a special rectangle
		● classify 2D shapes in various ways using mathematical properties such as reflective symmetry for 2D shapes	● can draw polygons with different properties
			● can classify shapes using correct mathematical vocabulary
				I can pick out 2D shapes with more than one line of symmetry. I can draw different polygons and know their mathematical names. I can draw all the shapes made from squares placed edge to edge and tell you what sort of polygon each one is.

⑥ Sums and differences				
Use knowledge of addition and subtraction facts and place value to derive sums and differences of pairs of multiples of 10, 100 or 1000	● use a range of mental methods of computation with addition and subtraction	● add and subtract two-digit numbers mentally	● uses a range of mental methods to quickly add multiples of 10, 100 or 1000 ● uses a range of mental methods to quickly find the difference between multiples of 10, 100 or 1000	*Because I know number facts such as 8 – 3 = 5, I know that 80 – 30 = 50. I can use this to work out calculations. I can find differences between numbers.*

BLOCK B

Unit 3 ▢ Securing number facts, understanding shape

Framework objectives	Assessment focuses		Success criteria for Year 4	Learning outcomes
	Level 4	**Level 3**		
⑦ Doubling and halving				
Identify the doubles of two-digit numbers; use to calculate doubles of multiples of 10 and 100 and derive the corresponding halves	• recognise and describe number relationships • use inverse operations	• add and subtract two-digit numbers mentally • use mental recall of the 2 multiplication table	• can work out doubles of two-digit numbers • knows that doubling and halving are inverse operations	*I can work out doubles of two-digit numbers. I know that doubling and halving are inverse operations.*
⑧ Making a 3D shape				

Visualise 3D objects from 2D drawings; make nets of common solids	• use the properties of 3D shapes, e.g.
	  ○ visualise shapes and recognise them in different orientations
	• make 3D models by linking given faces or edges
		• classify 3D shapes, e.g.
		  ○ recognise common 3D shapes, e.g. triangular prism, square-based pyramid
		  ○ relate 3D shapes to drawings and photographs of them, including from different viewpoints
		• begin to recognise nets of familiar 3D shapes, e.g. cube, cuboid, triangular prism, square-based pyramid
			• can visualise and name a shape from 2D drawings
			• can describe the properties of 3D shapes
			• can make a net of a 3D shape
				When I look at a drawing of a 3D shape I can work out what shapes I need to make its net, such as four triangles and a square to make a square-based pyramid.

⑨ Inverse operations				

Use knowledge of rounding, number operations and inverses to estimate and check calculations	• use inverse operations, e.g.
	  ○ use a calculator and inverse operations to find missing numbers
	• check the reasonableness of results with reference to the context or size of numbers
		• solve whole-number problems including those involving multiplication or division that may give rise to remainders, e.g.
		  ○ identify appropriate operations to use
			• knows that doubling and halving are inverse operations
			• knows that multiplication and division are inverse operations
				I can use inverse operations to help me check calculations. If you give me a number fact, I can tell you some related facts.

Activities ① and ②

Prior learning
Children can name common 2D shapes, draw a line of symmetry in a 2D shape and choose their own criterion for sorting a set of shapes. They recognise and describe some number patterns.

Framework objective
Identify and use patterns, relationships and properties of numbers or shapes; investigate a statement involving numbers and test it with examples

Vocabulary
problem, solution, explain, predict, pattern, relationship, property, add, subtract, multiply, divide, sum, total, difference, plus, minus, product, quotient, remainder, double, halve, factor, multiple, divisor, round, 2D, two-dimensional, regular, irregular, symmetrical, line of symmetry, polygon, equilateral triangle, isosceles triangle, quadrilateral, rectangle, square, oblong, hexagon, heptagon, octagon

Resources
Display page: Equation families
Resource sheet: Self-assessment
Classroom resources: triangular grid paper, calculators

① Properties of polygons

Discuss with the children ways of classifying polygons – for example, regular polygons; irregular polygons; polygons with right angles; polygons with one line of symmetry. Invite the children to choose a classification and draw some polygons on grid paper according to their chosen properties. For example: all irregular four-sided polygons; polygons that all have right angles; polygons that all have one line of symmetry; polygons that all have five sides, and so on. Ask the children to explain their drawings and ways of classifying them. Decide whether to use the self-assessment sheet for the children to record their achievements and what they need to do next.

Teacher support
Less confident learners: Restrict the choice of a criterion for drawing their polygons. The children could work with a partner or in a group with an adult.
More confident learners: Invite these children to compare their drawings with those of others in their group. Ask them to check each other's reasons for drawing and classifying. Can they add other polygons to their drawings?

Common misconception
Children are confused as to which polygons are regular and which are irregular. Show a variety of plastic, paper or drawn shapes, and explain that the regular polygons are those with angles and sides all equal. Ask children to sort the shapes into regular and irregular and explain how they know which is which.

Probing questions
● What is another name for a regular three-sided polygon?
● What is another name for a regular four-sided polygon?
● How do you know that this shape belongs in this group?

Next steps
Support: Ask the children to classify ready-drawn examples of a range of polygons. See also Year 4 Block B Unit 1 and Year 4 Block B Unit 2.
Extension: Encourage these children to investigate how many lines of symmetry different regular polygons have. Ask: *What statement or rule can be derived from this investigation?* See also Year 5 Block B Unit 1.

BLOCK B

② Equation families

Reveal the display page 'Equation families'. Ask the children to start with one equation and use their knowledge of number patterns to create a further family of equations. They should then ask a partner to identify patterns and what the equations have in common. Decide whether to use the self-assessment sheet for the children to record their achievements and what they need to do next.

Teacher support
Less confident learners: Restrict the starting points for equation families. Start with examples such as: 5 + 6 = 11; 11 − 6 = 5; 11 − 5 = 6; 50 + 60 = 110.
More confident learners: Encourage these children to generate larger equation families and check them with the aid of a calculator.

Common misconception
Children fail to see patterns between equations.
Ask children to work collaboratively to generate equation families. They could start with simple examples.

Probing questions
● How can this help you to know the answer to the other examples in the family?
● Give me another similar example.

Next steps
Support: Discuss ways of checking that equations are correct (for example, by using an inverse operation). See also Year 4 Block B Unit 2.
Extension: Include in the family of equations multiples of 10, 100 and 1000. See also Year 5 Block B Unit 1.

Activity ③

Prior learning	**Framework objective**
Children can identify the calculation needed to solve a one-step problem.	Solve one-step and two-step problems involving numbers, money or measures, including time; choose and carry out appropriate calculations, using calculator methods where appropriate
	Vocabulary
	problem, solution, calculator, calculate, calculation, answer, method
	Resources
	Worksheet: Will you be on time?
	Classroom resources: calculators

③ Will you be on time?

Discuss with the children ways to find and check solutions to problems: working mentally, using pencil and paper (especially if there are two steps to the problem), checking answers with a calculator even if you have used a pencil and paper or mental method first. Ask the children to look at the problems on the worksheet 'Will you be on time?' and discuss in pairs how they might solve each one. Ask them to complete the activity by finding each answer and writing down each method(s) they have used.

Teacher support
Less confident learners: Encourage these children to use more than one

method and cross-check answers. Ask an adult to discuss with the children the operations they should use and to help with jottings.
More confident learners: Ask these children to work with less confident learners to discuss methods of working. Alternatively, ask them to write similar word problems for the rest of the class to solve.

Common misconceptions
Children do not know which operation to use to solve the problem.
Help children to write a number sentence that will help to clarify what operation(s) to use to solve the problem.

Children lack secure knowledge of facts about time, such as 60 seconds = 1 minute, 24 hours in 1 day.
Ensure that children read the part of the question that helps them with this and ask them to write a table of equivalents in time.

Probing questions
● What number operation do you need to carry out for each question?
● Which problem will require you to calculate backwards from the time given in its first sentence? How many times will you have to do this?

Next steps
Support: Give the children a calculation and ask them to write their own word problem for it. Discuss how they decided which words to use. See also Year 4 Block B Units 1 and 2.
Extension: Invite these children to look at the problems written by others and try to solve them. See also Year 5 Block B Unit 1.

Activity ④

Prior learning
Children can recall multiplication and division facts for the 2-, 3-, 4-, 5-, 6- and 10-times tables. They can say a subtraction fact that is the inverse of an addition fact, and a multiplication fact that is the inverse of a division fact, and vice versa.

Framework objective
Derive and recall multiplication facts up to 10 × 10, the corresponding division facts and multiples of numbers to 10 up to the tenth multiple

Vocabulary
multiply, divide, factor, multiple, divisor, inverse operation

Resources
Interactive activity: Multiplication square
Resource sheet: Self-assessment
Classroom resources: counters, squared paper

④ Arrays and inverse operations

Display the interactive activity 'Multiplication square'. Highlight the answers to 1 × 8, 3 × 8, 7 × 8. Give pairs of children squared paper and ask them to group the number of dots that matches each highlighted number into a rectangular array. Ask them to write the 8-times tables facts and corresponding division facts for each array. For example, for 24, the children should write 3 × 8, 8 × 3, 24 ÷ 8 and 24 ÷ 3. They could then choose their own answers for other times tables to show different facts. Decide whether to use the self-assessment sheet for children to record their achievements and what they need to do next.

Unit 3 📖 Securing number facts, understanding shape

Teacher support

Less confident learners: Let these children use familiar times tables, drawing an array for each answer. Help them to write the related number sentences.

More confident learners: Invite these children to make a group of arrays that represent 12 (4 rows of 3, 3 rows of 4, 2 rows of 6, 6 rows of 2, 12 rows of 1 and 1 row of 12). Now ask them to identify the factors of 12.

Common misconception

Children are insecure in deriving division facts from the corresponding multiplication facts.

Use rectangles to practise division:

$21 \div 3 = 7$ and $21 \div 7 = 3$. There are 21 small rectangles divided into 3 rows of 7 or 7 rows of 3. Children could colour each row a different colour to illustrate 3 rows of 7 = 21. A partner could colour each column a different colour to illustrate 7 columns of 3.

Probing questions

● Which multiplication and division facts can you remember easily? How can they help you to learn the tricky ones?

● What are some multiplication and division facts for 24? How can drawing arrays of 24 help you to find out?

Next steps

Support: Give pairs of children a number of counters (such as 12 or 24). Ask one child to arrange them in an array to show multiplication and division facts. The other child can write them down. See also Year 3 Block B Unit 3.

Extension: Combine arrays to show multiplication and division facts for larger numbers, such as $10 \times 10 + 2 \times 10 = 12 \times 10$. See also Year 5 Block B Unit 1.

Activity ⑤

Prior learning

Children can identify and draw regular and irregular 2D polygons. They can identify line symmetry and can draw a line of symmetry in a 2D shape.

Framework objectives

● Report solutions to puzzles and problems, giving explanations and reasoning orally and in writing, using diagrams and symbols

● Draw polygons and classify them by identifying their properties, including their line symmetry

Vocabulary

problem, solution, 2D, two-dimensional, regular, irregular, symmetrical, line of symmetry, polygon, equilateral triangle, isosceles triangle, quadrilateral, rectangle, square, oblong, hexagon, heptagon, octagon

Resources

Worksheet: Report on polygons
Classroom resources: isometric and squared paper, mirrors, plastic polygons

⑤ Report on polygons

Provide the children with grid paper and ask them to complete the worksheet 'Report on polygons'. Ask them to report what they have done to another pair or to the rest of the class.

Teacher support

Less confident learners: Look at examples of each kind of polygon with the children before asking them to draw their own. Talk about the shapes' properties as the children complete their drawings.

More confident learners: Extend the work to include heptagons and octagons.

Common misconception

Children do not recognise the number of lines of symmetry in different regular shapes.

Provide mirrors and encourage children to check using plastic templates of regular polygons. They could also cut out paper polygons and fold them to identify lines of symmetry.

Probing questions

- Which of your polygons has a right angle? How do you know?
- Which of your polygons has more than one right angle?

Next steps

Support: Invite the children to collect examples of different triangles to reinforce the idea that not all triangles are equilateral. Repeat for quadrilaterals and hexagons. See also Year 4 Block B Units 1 and 2.

Extension: Ask the children to draw hexagons with 0, 1, 2, 3, 4, 5 and 6 lines of symmetry, reporting on their results to the rest of the group. See also Year 5 Block B Unit 1.

Activity ⑥

Prior learning
Children can recall addition and subtraction facts for each number to 20. They can multiply a unit number by 10, 100 and 1000.

Framework objective
Use knowledge of addition and subtraction facts and place value to derive sums and differences of pairs of multiples of 10, 100 or 1000

Vocabulary
add, subtract, multiply, divide, sum, total, difference, plus, minus

Resources
Interactive activity: Sums and differences
Classroom resources: whiteboards and pens, place value or digit cards

⑥ Sums and differences

Reveal the interactive activity 'Sums and differences'. In this activity the children are asked to find the solutions to a range of questions involving addition or subtraction calculations.

Teacher support

Less confident learners: Ask these children to highlight the digits other than zero on their whiteboards – to reinforce how knowing facts to 10 can help with larger numbers.

More confident learners: Ask these children to find the difference between large numbers that are close together, such as 1980 and 2020.

Common misconception

Children's grasp of place value is weak.

Provide oral practice in counting in 10s, 100s and 1000s. Ask quick-fire questions on finding differences of multiples of 10, 100 or 1000.

▶ **Probing questions**
- Explain how you worked out the sum/difference of those two numbers.
- Would you use the same method for these numbers?

Next steps
Support: Provide the children with plenty of practice in adding numbers to 20. See also Year 3 Block B Unit 3.
Extension: Challenge these children to devise a game using place value or digit cards to generate numbers and then find sums and differences. See also Year 5 Block B Unit 3.

Activity ⑦

Prior learning Children can double and halve numbers to 20 and recognise multiples of 10 and 100.	**Framework objective** Identify the doubles of two-digit numbers; use to calculate doubles of multiples of 10 and 100 and derive the corresponding halves **Vocabulary** double, halve, calculate, multiple, inverse operation **Resources** **Interactive activity:** Function machine **Resource sheets:** 1-9 digit cards, Place value arrow cards **Classroom resources:** whiteboards and pens

⑦ Doubling and halving

Invite a child to choose a number between 10 and 20. Ask the class to double it. Continue until the answer is close to 500, without exceeding it. Each time an answer is offered, ask the children to show their methods on their whiteboards. For example, for a start number of 17: $17 + 17 = (10 \times 2) + (7 \times 2) = 20 + 14 = 34$; $34 \times 2 = 30 \times 2 + 4 \times 2 = 60 + 8 = 68$; $68 + 68 = (60 \times 2) + (8 \times 2) = 120 + 16 = 136$; $136 \times 2 = (100 \times 2) + (30 \times 2) + (6 \times 2) = 200 + 60 + 12 = 272$. Repeat for halving even numbers between 400 and 500, stopping when an odd number is reached.

Teacher support
Less confident learners: Use the interactive activity 'Function machine': doubling is represented by 'X + X = Y' and halving is represented by 'Y − X = X'. For example, $16 + 16 = 32$; $32 − 16 = 16$. The children should then write an equivalent example on their whiteboards: $16 \times 2 = 32$ and $32 \div 2 = 16$. Ensure that they recognise the doubling and halving that is taking place.
More confident learners: Ask these children to start with a two-digit odd number (for example, 35). Ask them to explain to a partner how to halve this number: half of 30 = 15 and half of 5 = 2.5. So half of 35 is 17.5.

Common misconception
Children do not recognise that doubling two-digit numbers involves two steps. Some children may not appreciate that it is necessary to double the tens, double the units and then add both together; others may not be able to carry all this information in their heads and may therefore make mistakes in their calculations. Encourage these children to make jottings on their whiteboards (or use paper and pencils) and check their answers.

BLOCK B

Probing questions
● When you have doubled a number and then halve the new number you get back to the original number. Can you explain why this is? (Doubling and halving are inverse operations).
● How can you check your answer when you have doubled/halved a two-digit number?

Next steps
Support: Ask the children to pick a digit card at random and double it, double the answer (and so on) as far they can go. See also Year 4 Block B Unit 2.
Extension: Ask these children to make four-digit numbers from place value arrow cards and then challenge a partner to halve the number repeatedly until an odd number is reached. See also Year 5 Block B Unit 1.

Activity ⑧

Prior learning
Children can name common 2D and 3D shapes, and recognise a 3D shape from a 2D drawing of it.

Framework objective
Visualise 3D objects from 2D drawings; make nets of common solids

Vocabulary
3D, three-dimensional, 2D, two-dimensional, net, construct, vertex, vertices, face, edge, polygon, equilateral triangle, isosceles triangle, quadrilateral, rectangle, square, oblong

Resources
Resource sheet: Self-assessment
Classroom resources: paper, rulers, pencils, range of 2D and 3D shapes

⑧ Making a 3D shape

Ask the children to work in pairs. One child should describe the properties of a square-based pyramid and their partner should listen and draw its net. They then cut out the net and make the solid shape. When they have completed this, decide whether to use the self-assessment sheet for the children to record their achievements and what they need to do next.

Teacher support
Less confident learners: Ask an adult to draw the net as the group describes what to draw. If necessary, use a 3D square-based pyramid for reference and ask the children to describe what they see before asking them to describe it from memory.
More confident learners: Ask pairs of children to describe and draw the net of a triangular-based pyramid.

Common misconceptions
Children have difficulty using 3D shape vocabulary (for example, 'vertices', 'edges', 'faces').
Provide opportunities to use vocabulary through 'guess the shape' games.

Children confuse pyramids and prisms.
Provide children with opportunities to compare these two 3D shapes, listing their differences and similarities.

Probing questions
● What is the difference between the net of a triangular-based pyramid and that of a triangular prism?

● What is the difference between nets of a square-based pyramid and a cuboid?

Next steps
Support: Provide nets of a cube and a cuboid. Discuss what is the same and what is different. Ask the children to construct the shapes, using the nets, working in a group with an adult if possible. See also Year 4 Block B Unit 1.
Extension: Invite the children to make a net of a triangular prism and construct the 3D shape. See also Year 5 Block B Unit 1.

Activity ⑨

Prior learning
Children can use inverse operations to check calculations.

Framework objectives
● Use knowledge of rounding, number operations and inverses to estimate and check calculations
● **Derive and recall multiplication facts up to 10 × 10, the corresponding division facts and multiples of numbers to 10 up to the tenth multiple**

Vocabulary
check, calculation, equation, operation, inverse, answer, method, explain, relationship, rule, add, subtract, sum, total, difference, plus, minus

Resources
Interactive activity: Inverse operations (multiplication and division)
Classroom resources: calculators

⑨ Inverse operations

Write on the board: $56 \div 8 = 7$. Ask the children to write the corresponding multiplication fact for this division fact. Discuss that multiplication is the inverse of division. Ask: *How could you use this to check that the answer to 55 × 4 is 220?* Let the children work through the questions on the interactive activity 'Inverse operations (multiplication and division)'.

Teacher support
Less confident learners: Let these children work in a group with adult support.
More confident learners: Ask these children to generate examples of their own. They may wish to use a calculator as the main objective is to match equations showing inverse operations.

Common misconception
Children lack secure knowledge of multiplication and division facts.
By playing games and completing quizzes, provide children with many different opportunities to practise multiplication and the corresponding division tables.

Probing questions
● If you know that 25 × 4 = 200 and 200 ÷ 4 is 25, how can this help you to work out 25 × 8? Tell me the corresponding division fact.
● How many 25s are there in 1000? How did you work this out? What is the corresponding division fact?

Next steps
Support: Ask the children to play a matching game where one set of cards has multiplication facts on it and the other set has the corresponding division facts. See also Year 4 Block B Unit 1.
Extension: Give these children a time limit in which to generate their own examples. See also Year 5 Block B Unit 1.

◻ # Periodic assessment

These activities can be used at any time during the teaching of this block to assess those children that you think have achieved the objective. A grid highlighting the related assessment focuses and expected learning outcomes for each activity can be found on the CD-ROM.

Multiples

Framework objective
Derive and recall multiplication facts up to 10 × 10, the corresponding division facts and multiples of numbers to 10 up to the tenth multiple

Learning outcomes
- I can recall multiplication facts to 10 × 10 and quickly say the corresponding division facts.
- I can work out division facts for 1-, 2-, 3-, 4-, 5-, 6- and 10-times tables.

Display the interactive activity 'Multiplication square'. Highlight a square and challenge children, in turn, to quickly tell you multiplication facts for that number. Select questions carefully for each child (for example, ask more confident learners to tell you facts for a whole row or column). Next, give each child a copy of the worksheet 'Multiples', which assesses their understanding of corresponding multiplication and division facts. Customise this sheet according to children's progress towards level 3 or level 4 objectives. To begin, check that they know what is meant by a multiplication or division sentence. Work through one example of each with them.

Shopping

Framework objective
Solve one-step and two-step problems involving numbers, money or measures, including time; choose and carry out appropriate calculations, using calculator methods where appropriate

Learning outcomes
- I can work out how to solve problems with one or two steps.
- I can decide what calculation to work out and whether a calculator will help me.
- I can think about the numbers in a calculation and choose a good way to do the calculation.

Ask the children to complete the worksheet 'Shopping'. They may use a calculator to complete this activity.

Sorting shapes

Framework objective
Draw polygons and classify them by identifying their properties, including their line symmetry

Learning outcomes
- I can use what I know about triangles to group them into equilateral triangles, isosceles triangles and other triangles.
- I can pick out triangles that have a right angle from other triangles.
- I can recognise symmetrical polygons, including those with more than one line of symmetry.

Ask the children to complete the worksheet 'Sorting shapes'. If necessary, provide them with extra copies of the worksheet which they can use to cut out the shapes and fold them in order to check on the lines of symmetry. Encourage them to suggest different ways to sort the shapes on the sheet.

Name	Date

Multiples

■ Here are some multiples from the 6 to 9 multiplication tables. For each multiple write two multiplication sentences and two division sentences.

Multiple	Multiplication sentences	Division sentences
30		
54		
72		
63		
48		
56		
42		
35		
90		
40		

How easy?

Red

Amber

Green

How do you think you have done?

_____

_____

Name	Date

Shopping

You may use a calculator.

1. Three transactions, A, B and C, are made in a shop. Find the total cost of each.

A.   6.50
   + £12.00
   _____
   _____

B.   99p
   + 76p
   _____
   _____

C.   £9.95
   + £0.88
   _____
   _____

2. For each of the three transactions, find the change received by the customer.

A. The customer pays with £20. _____

B. The customer pays with £5. _____

C. The customer pays with £18. _____

Explain how you found and checked your answers.

_____

_____

3. The shop sells six items at these prices:

   £6.50   £12.00   £0.99   76p   £9.95   £0.88

◼ Show a written method of calculating the cost of five of each item.

_____

_____

_____

_____

_____

◼ Now you may use a calculator to check your answers if you wish.

How easy?

Red
Amber
Green

How do you think you have done?

_____

_____

| Name | Date |

Sorting shapes

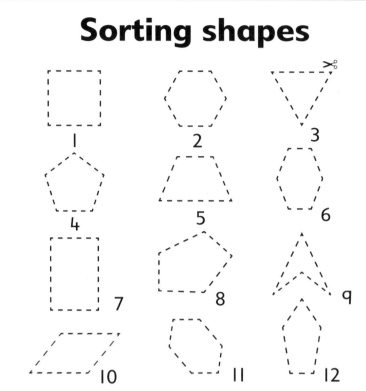

■ Look at each shape and complete the table. (You can cut out the shapes if you need to.)

Shape	Regular or irregular polygon?	Name of shape	Number of lines of symmetry
1			
2			
3			
4			
5			
6			
7			
8			
9			
10			
11			
12			

How easy?

Red
Amber
Green

How do you think you have done?

_____

_____

BLOCK C
Handling data and measures

Expected prior learning
Check that children can already:
- consider a question and develop a response by referring to relevant data
- make and use lists, tables and simple bar charts to organise and interpret the information
- use Venn diagrams or Carroll diagrams to sort data and objects using more than one criterion
- recall the relationships between kilometres and metres, metres and centimetres, kilograms and grams, litres and millilitres
- choose and use appropriate units to estimate, measure and record length and weight
- measure and draw to a suitable degree of accuracy, for example measure length to the nearest half centimetre and weight to the nearest half division on the scales.

Objectives overview
The text in this diagram identifies the focus of mathematics learning within the block.

Key aspects of learning
- Enquiry
- Creative thinking
- Information processing
- Evaluation
- Communication

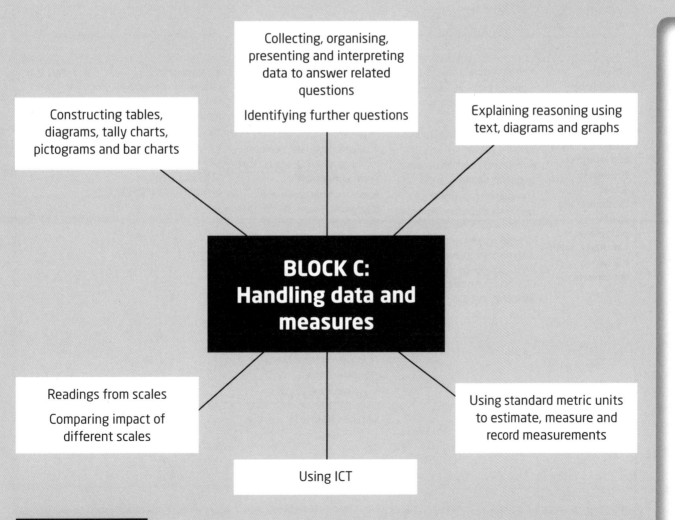

Collecting, organising, presenting and interpreting data to answer related questions

Identifying further questions

Constructing tables, diagrams, tally charts, pictograms and bar charts

Explaining reasoning using text, diagrams and graphs

BLOCK C: Handling data and measures

Readings from scales

Comparing impact of different scales

Using standard metric units to estimate, measure and record measurements

Using ICT

Unit 1   Handling data and measures

Introduction

In this unit, children develop their data handling skills by collecting, organising, presenting, analysing and interpreting data. They work in groups so that they develop their skills in working together, sharing tasks and ensuring that the job is done in the time allowed. They make decisions about what data to collect and how they will go about this. Work on measures is focused on length. Children measure to the nearest unit, including to the nearest millimetre, and can record this in decimal form.

Framework objectives	Assessment focuses		Success criteria for Year 4	Learning outcomes
	Level 4	Level 3		
① Conducting a survey ② Collecting data ③ Reporting results				
Suggest a line of enquiry and the strategy needed to follow it; collect, organise and interpret selected information to find answers	• develop own strategies for solving problems, e.g. • make their own suggestions of ways to tackle a range of problems	• select the mathematics they use in a wider range of classroom activities, e.g. • use classroom discussions to break into a problem, recognising similarities to previous work • put the problem into their own words	• thinks about and discusses how to collect information that is relevant to the problem or question posed	*I can think about an experiment, predict what might happen and decide how I could go about finding out whether it is true.*
Answer a question by identifying what data to collect; organise, present, analyse and interpret the data in tables, diagrams, tally charts, pictograms and bar charts, using ICT where appropriate	• collect discrete data, e.g. • given a problem, suggest possible answers and data to collect • record discrete data using a frequency table • represent collected data in frequency diagrams, e.g. • suggest an appropriate frequency diagram to represent particular data, e.g. decide whether a bar chart, Venn diagram or pictogram would be most appropriate and for pictograms use one symbol to represent, say, 2, 5, 10 or 100	• gather information, e.g. • decide what data to collect to answer a question, e.g. what is the most common way to travel to school • make appropriate choices for recording data, e.g. a tally chart or frequency table • construct bar charts and pictograms, where the symbol represents a group of units, e.g. • decide how best to represent data, e.g. whether a bar chart, Venn diagram or pictogram would show the information most clearly • decide upon an appropriate scale for a graph, e.g. labelled divisions of 2, or, for a pictogram, one symbol to represent 2 or 5 • use Venn and Carroll diagrams to record their sorting and classifying of information	• knows what information needs to be collected and can record results of a survey • is able to present this information in the form of a block graph, pictogram or bar chart	*I can collect data and put it in a table to help me explore an idea and find out more about it.*

Unit 1 📖 Handling data and measures

Framework objectives	Assessment focuses		Success criteria for Year 4	Learning outcomes
	Level 4	**Level 3**		
① **Conducting a survey** ② **Collecting data** ③ **Reporting results**				
Report solutions to puzzles and problems, giving explanations and reasoning orally and in writing, using diagrams and symbols	● present information and results in a clear and organised way, e.g. ● organise written work, e.g. record results in order ● begin to work in an organised way from the start ● consider appropriate units ● use related vocabulary accurately	● discuss their mathematical work and begin to explain their thinking, e.g. ● use appropriate mathematical vocabulary ● talk about their findings by referring to their written work ● use and interpret mathematical symbols and diagrams	● presents information and results using diagrams and graphs	*I can tell people what I have found out and show some graphs to back up my conclusions.*
④ **Watch my weight!**				
Choose and use standard metric units and their abbreviations when estimating, measuring and recording length, weight and capacity; know the meaning of 'kilo', 'centi' and 'milli' and, where appropriate, use decimal notation to record measurements (e.g. 1.3m or 0.6kg)	● choose and use appropriate units and instruments ● interpret, with appropriate accuracy, numbers on a range of measuring instruments, e.g. ● measure a length using mm, to within 2mm	● use non-standard units and standard metric units of length, capacity and mass in a range of contexts, e.g. ● measure a length to the nearest ½cm ● read simple scales, e.g. increments of 2, 5 or 10	● estimates and measures mass using standard units	*I can measure lengths, weights and times to help me find out more about a question I am exploring.*
Interpret intervals and divisions on partially numbered scales and record readings accurately, where appropriate to the nearest tenth of a unit	● interpret, with appropriate accuracy, numbers on a range of measuring instruments	● use non-standard units and standard metric units of length, capacity and mass in a range of contexts, e.g. ● read simple scales, e.g. increments of 2, 5 or 10	● reads weights in grams and kilograms on partially numbered scales	*I can measure lengths to the nearest half centimetre, weights in grams and kilograms, and times in seconds.*

BLOCK C

Activities ① – ③

Prior learning
Children can consider a question and develop a response by referring to relevant data. They can make and use lists, tables and simple bar charts to organise and interpret the information.

Framework objectives
- Suggest a line of enquiry and the strategy needed to follow it; collect, organise and interpret selected information to find answers
- **Answer a question by identifying what data to collect; organise, present, analyse and interpret the data in tables, diagrams, tally charts, pictograms and bar charts, using ICT where appropriate**
- Report solutions to puzzles and problems, giving explanations and reasoning orally and in writing, using diagrams and symbols

Vocabulary
problem, solution, explain, reasoning, reason, predict, classify, represent, interpret, data, information, survey, questionnaire, graph, chart, table, diagram, horizontal axis, vertical axis, axes, label, title, scale, interval, pictogram, bar chart, tally chart, greatest/least value

Resources
Interactive activity: Class survey
Worksheets: Class survey (1), (2) and (3)
Resource sheets: Bar chart template, Pictogram template, Block graph template

① Conducting a survey

Give each child a copy of the worksheet 'Class survey (1)' and prepare the interactive activity 'Class survey'. Tell the children that they are going to carry out a survey about their leisure time. Each child will choose from: Sport, Watching TV, Playing on the computer or Other. Invite a volunteer to come to the board and enter these four categories into the left-hand column of the on-screen data table. When everyone has voted on their favourite leisure activity, invite another volunteer to use the pop-up keypad to enter the relevant numbers into the right-hand column of the data table. Finally, click 'create bar chart' to see a bar chart showing the results of the survey.

Teacher support
Less confident learners: Ask an adult to describe to the children what is happening throughout the whole-class activity and to ask the probing questions.
More confident learners: Invite these children to interpret the results from this survey.

Common misconception
Children do not realise that the first results of a survey do not necessarily indicate what the final outcome is going to be.
Encourage comments on the progress of the vote. Ask which is most/least popular activity after 10 votes, after 15 votes, after 20 votes (and so on). Encourage predictions of the final outcome of the vote.

Probing questions
- What is the most/least popular leisure activity at the moment?
- Was this a good way to collect the data? Why/why not?
- What does the graph of most popular leisure activities tell us?

Next steps
Support: Discuss alternative ways of collecting data. See also Year 3 Block C.
Extension: Discuss next steps in this activity. See also Year 4 Block C Unit 2.

② Collecting data

Give each child a copy of the worksheet 'Class survey (2)'. The whole class should work together on the first part of this activity. Tell the children that they are going to do a more detailed survey about the most popular leisure activity in the class. Discuss whether to use a tally chart or frequency table. Work through the survey tasks on the activity sheet together. Finally, discuss the options for presenting information: pictogram, bar chart, block graph.

Teacher support
Less confident learners: The children could work in mixed ability groups. Alternatively, ensure that an adult is available to guide less confident learners.
More confident learners: Ask these children to plan a survey about favourite school subjects, collecting data using a tally chart. Encourage them to plan and work independently.

Common misconception
Children are unsure how to check that everyone has voted and only voted once.
Ask children to count the total number of votes. Does it match the number of children in the class today?

Probing questions
● What is this frequency table/tally chart going to tell us?
● How will we collect the information?

Next steps
Support: Encourage the children to organise and collect data within their class or group on a different subject. Support them in producing a tally chart. See also Year 3 Block C.
Extension: Ask the group to check and compare results of their independent surveys. See also Year 4 Block C Unit 2.

③ Reporting results

Organise the children to work in pairs or groups. Give each child a copy of the worksheet 'Class survey (3)'. The children will also need copies of the completed tally chart or frequency table from Activity 2. Ask each group to discuss how they want to present their information: block graph, pictogram or bar chart. They should then use the gathered information and produce their chart/graph/pictogram using one of the resource sheets 'Bar chart template', 'Pictogram template' or 'Block graph template'.

Teacher support
Less confident learners: Either ask these children to work in mixed ability groups or ensure that an adult is available to guide the less confident learners.
More confident learners: Invite these children to report on their own independent surveys.

Common misconception
Children are unsure how to label the axes of a chart or graph.
Ask children to consider the kind of chart or graph they have chosen to produce, and discuss what information will be needed to make it easily understood.

Probing questions
● If you are doing a pictogram, how will you represent a vote? Will each represent one vote or two or more?
● On your bar chart/block graph, how many votes does one bar or block represent?

▷ **Next steps**
Support: Produce simple graphs based on other data that has been collected as suggested in the previous activity. See also Year 3 Block C.
▢ **Extension:** Ask these children to present, analyse and interpret data from surveys. See Year 4 Block C Unit 2.

Activity ④

BLOCK C

Prior learning
Children can recall the relationships between kilometres and metres, metres and centimetres, kilograms and grams, litres and millilitres. They choose and use appropriate units to estimate, measure and record length and weight.

Framework objectives
● **Choose and use standard metric units and their abbreviations when estimating, measuring and recording length, weight and capacity; know the meaning of 'kilo', 'centi' and 'milli' and, where appropriate, use decimal notation to record measurements (for example, 1.3m or 0.6kg)**
● Interpret intervals and divisions on partially numbered scales and record readings accurately, where appropriate to the nearest tenth of a unit

Vocabulary
metric unit, standard unit, millimetre (mm), centimetre (cm), metre (m), kilogram (kg), gram (g), litre (l), millilitre (ml)

Resources
Resource sheet: Self-assessment
Classroom resources: a variety of fruits (several different types for each group), weighing scales (for each group)

④ Watch my weight!

Ask the children to work in groups of four to six and to choose what roles each person will play (for example scribe, reporter, leader and so on). As a group they need to find a way to estimate and weigh each piece of fruit. Tell them to put the fruit in order from least to greatest mass and then record their work so that they can report back to the rest of the class. Decide whether to use the self-assessment sheet for the children to record their achievements and next steps.

Teacher support
Less confident learners: Let these children work in groups with adult support.
More confident learners: Ask these children to find other items in the classroom that weigh about the same as each piece of fruit.

Common misconception
Children confuse kilograms and grams.
Show children something that weighs about 1 kilogram (for example, a bag of sugar) and something that weighs about 1 gram (for example, a centimetre cube). Provide plenty of opportunities for children to weigh a variety of items.

Probing questions
● Estimate the weight of this bag of apples. How did knowing the weight of one apple help you estimate the weight of the bag?
● Would you estimate the weight of a banana in grams or kilograms? Why?

Next steps
Support: Ask the children to estimate and weigh other items in the classroom. Decide whether to record in grams or kilograms. See also Year 3 Block D Unit 2.
Extension: Ask these children to estimate and weigh all the apples/oranges in the classroom. Decide upon the most appropriate unit for recording the result. See also Year 4 Block D Unit 1.

Unit 2   Handling data and measures

Introduction

In this unit children collect, organise, present and interpret data to answer related questions, identifying further questions. They construct tables, diagrams, tally charts, pictograms and bar charts. They can explain their reasoning using text, diagrams and graphs. Children read from scales and compare the impact of different scales. They use standard metric units to estimate, measure and record measurements.

Framework objectives	Assessment focuses		Success criteria for Year 4	Learning outcomes
	Level 4	Level 3		
① Birthday seasons ② Birthday months ③ Venn and Carroll diagrams				
Suggest a line of enquiry and the strategy needed to follow it; collect, organise and interpret selected information to find answers	• develop own strategies for solving problems, e.g. • make their own suggestions of ways to tackle a range of problems • make connections to previous work • pose and answer questions related to a problem • check answers and ensure solutions make sense in the context of the problem • review their work and approaches	• select the mathematics they use in a wider range of classroom activities, e.g. • use classroom discussions to break into a problem, recognising similarities to previous work • put the problem into their own words • choose their own equipment appropriate to the task, including calculators • try different approaches and find ways of overcoming difficulties that arise when they are solving problems	• thinks about and discusses how to collect information that is relevant to the problem or question posed • decides what form of presentation is appropriate after considering options	*I can think of a question to ask about some information and organise the information to help me find out more about it.*
Answer a question by identifying what data to collect; organise, present, analyse and interpret the data in tables, diagrams, tally charts, pictograms and bar charts, using ICT where appropriate	• collect discrete data, e.g. • given a problem, suggest possible answers and data to collect • record discrete data using a frequency table • represent collected data in frequency diagrams, e.g. • suggest an appropriate frequency diagram to represent particular data, e.g. decide whether a bar chart, Venn diagram or pictogram would be most appropriate and for pictograms use one symbol to represent, say, 2, 5, 10 or 100 • continue to use Venn and Carroll diagrams to record their sorting and classifying of information	• gather information, e.g. • decide what data to collect to answer a question, e.g. what is the most common way to travel to school? • make appropriate choices for recording data, e.g. a tally chart or frequency table • construct bar charts and pictograms, where the symbol represents a group of units, e.g. • decide how best to represent data, e.g. whether a bar chart, Venn diagram or pictogram would show the information most clearly • decide upon an appropriate scale for a graph, e.g. labelled divisions of 2, or, for a pictogram, one symbol to represent 2 or 5 • use Venn and Carroll diagrams to record their sorting and classifying of information	• knows what information needs to be collected and can decide how to record results of a survey, e.g. in the form of a tally chart or frequency chart • is able to present this information in the form of a block graph, pictogram or bar chart	*I can choose from tables, diagrams, tally charts, pictograms and bar charts to show data so that they are easy to understand.*

Unit 2 ⬜ Handling data and measures

Framework objectives	Assessment focuses		Success criteria for Year 4	Learning outcomes
	Level 4	**Level 3**		
① **Birthday seasons** ② **Birthday months** ③ **Venn and Carroll diagrams**				
Report solutions to puzzles and problems, giving explanations and reasoning orally and in writing, using diagrams and symbols	• present information and results in a clear and organised way, e.g. ● organise written work, e.g. record results in order ● begin to work in an organised way from the start ● consider appropriate units ● use related vocabulary accurately	• discuss their mathematical work and begin to explain their thinking, e.g. ● use appropriate mathematical vocabulary ● talk about their findings by referring to their written work • use and interpret mathematical symbols and diagrams	• presents information and results orally and in writing, using diagrams and symbols	*I can explain how I solved a puzzle using a diagram to help me.*
④ **Measurement dilemmas**				
Choose and use standard metric units and their abbreviations when estimating, measuring and recording length, weight and capacity; know the meaning of 'kilo', 'centi' and 'milli' and, where appropriate, use decimal notation to record measurements (e.g. 1.3m or 0.6kg)	• choose and use appropriate units and instruments • interpret, with appropriate accuracy, numbers on a range of measuring instruments, e.g. ● measure a length using mm, to within 2mm	• use non-standard units and standard metric units of length, capacity and mass in a range of contexts, e.g. ● measure a length to the nearest ½cm	• can estimate length in standard metric units • can order objects according to their length	*I can measure carefully lengths to the nearest half centimetre so that my measurement is accurate.*
⑤ **What's my line?**				
Interpret intervals and divisions on partially numbered scales and record readings accurately, where appropriate to the nearest tenth of a unit	• interpret, with appropriate accuracy, numbers on a range of measuring instruments	• use non-standard units and standard metric units of length, capacity and mass in a range of contexts, e.g. ● read simple scales, e.g. increments of 2, 5 or 10	• can interpret intervals and divisions on partially numbered scales and record readings accurately, where appropriate to the nearest tenth of a unit	*I can use different kinds of rulers and measuring tapes to measure lengths accurately.*
⑥ **Data handling problems**				
Compare the impact of representations where scales have intervals of differing step size	• represent collected data in frequency diagrams, e.g. ● suggest an appropriate frequency diagram to represent particular data, e.g. decide whether a bar chart, Venn diagram or pictogram would be most appropriate and for pictograms use one symbol to represent, say, 2, 5, 10 or 100 • construct simple line graphs	• extract and interpret information presented in simple tables, lists, bar charts and pictograms, e.g. ● read scales labelled in twos, fives and tens, including reading between labelled divisions such as a point halfway between 40 and 50 or 8 and 10 • construct bar charts and pictograms, where the symbol represents a group of units	• recognises, interprets correctly and compares the impact of representations on graphs where scales have intervals of differing step size	*I can compare graphs with different scales and decide which is the most useful.*

■SCHOLASTIC

Activities ① – ③

BLOCK C

Prior learning

Children can consider a question and develop a response by referring to relevant data. They can make and use lists, tables and simple bar charts to organise and interpret the information. They can use Venn diagrams or Carroll diagrams to sort data and objects using more than one criterion.

Framework objectives

- Suggest a line of enquiry and the strategy needed to follow it; collect, organise and interpret selected information to find answers
- **Answer a question by identifying what data to collect; organise, present, analyse and interpret the data in tables, diagrams, tally charts, pictograms and bar charts, using ICT where appropriate**
- Report solutions to puzzles and problems, giving explanations and reasoning orally and in writing, using diagrams and symbols

Vocabulary

problem, solution, explain, reasoning, reason, predict, classify, represent, interpret, data, information, survey, questionnaire, graph, chart, table, diagram, horizontal axis, vertical axis, axes, label, title, scale, interval, pictogram, bar chart, tally chart, greatest/least value

Resources

Interactive activity: Birthday seasons
Resource sheets: Self-assessment, Venn diagram template, Carroll diagram template
Classroom resources: sticky notes, skipping ropes

① Birthday seasons

Ask the children which month their birthday is in. Ask: *What season is that?* Divide the class into groups of about six and ask one person in each group to be the scribe. Ask the children to prepare a tally chart to show which season each group member was born in. Ask pairs to collect the totals for each season from each group. They then input the information into the interactive activity 'Birthday seasons'. Click 'create bar chart' to produce a bar chart of the data. Invite the children to discuss what conclusions they can draw from the graph.

Teacher support

Less confident learners: Let these children work in mixed ability groups. Provide adult support to encourage them to enter into the activity and discussion.
More confident learners: Ask these children to present their conclusions orally before the less confident learners. Encourage them to suggest other questions that they could ask about this data.

Common misconception

Children are unsure how to produce or read a tally chart.
Remind children of how to keep a tally by making a mark for each event or answer, and that every fifth mark is drawn across the previous four. Provide opportunities for children to make tallies - for example, ask them to record how many in their class are having packed lunch and how many school dinners.

Probing questions

- How does the tally chart show how many people were born in autumn?
- Which season has the most/fewest birthdays?
- Can we find out which month has the most/fewest birthdays?

Next steps

Support: Ask these children to conduct a survey (with adult support) relating to birthday months rather than seasons. See also Year 4 Block C Unit 1.
Extension: Ask children to suggest a further line of enquiry and to work with a partner or group to collect data from the class. See also Year 4 Block C Unit 3.

② Birthday months

Give each child a sticky note and ask them to write their birthday month on it. Ask them to suggest how the sticky notes could be used to show how many children have birthdays in each month. Then write the first letter of each month on the board in either a vertical or horizontal line and ask the children to stick their notes in the correct position. Invite them to use this data to present a more permanent record of findings: as a block graph, a bar chart or pictogram. *What can you say about your results? When are most/fewest boys/girls born?* Decide whether to use the self-assessment sheet for the children to record their achievements and next steps.

Teacher support
Less confident learners: Give these children specific support depending upon what kind of representation they are going to make.
More confident learners: Ask children to present their results in two different ways (for example, by producing two different graphs with different step sizes).

Common misconception
Children do not realise that the symbols in a pictogram must be all the same size, shape and colour.
Provide squared paper for children to use when drawing pictograms to help them to keep size consistent. Also, show how pictograms are represented by a computer program. Emphasise that symbols for a particular pictogram are all identical.

Probing questions
● Are there any months when this class has no birthdays? Should we still include those months? Why?
● What do you think is the best step size to use for this particular chart? Why?
● Why would a step size of 10/20 not work for this data?

Next steps
Support: Let these children work in groups with adult support. Invite them to suggest their own lines of enquiry for collecting data and representing results. See also Year 3 Block C.
Extension: Encourage the children to work independently on their own lines of enquiry. See also Year 5 Block C.

③ Venn and Carroll diagrams

Ask a group of six or eight children to come to the front and sort themselves into two sets: girls and nine-year-olds. Ask: *Will some children fall into two categories? How can we represent this on a Venn diagram?* Use large skipping ropes on the floor to help sort the children. Next, divide the class into groups of six, seven or eight. Ask the children to repeat the activity and find other ways of sorting; recording results on resource sheets 'Venn diagram template' and 'Carroll diagram template'. Decide whether to use the self-assessment sheet for the children to record their achievements and next steps.

Teacher support
Less confident learners: Ask an adult to support the children in recording results.
More confident learners: Invite these children to produce a frequency chart and a Carroll diagram that represents the whole class.

Common misconception
Children are unsure how to transfer information onto Venn or Carroll diagrams.
When preparing to draw a Carroll diagram or Venn diagram, children could first list the data under each of the headings that they will be using. For example, for

BLOCK C

multiples of 2 and multiples of 3, they could list numbers that are multiples of 2, multiples of 3, multiples of both 2 and 3 and multiples of neither. They can then make sure that numbers only occur in one place (they keep numbers in 'both', but delete duplicates from the other lists) and draw the Venn or Carroll diagram.

Probing questions
● Where will we write 'boys' and 'girls' on this Carroll diagram? Where will we write '8-year-olds' and '9-year-olds'?
● Jane is a nine-year-old girl. Where should we place her on this diagram?

Next steps
Support: Ask these children to sort shapes onto a Venn or Carroll diagram with headings already written. See also Year 3 Block C.
Extension: Ask the children to complete a table of how many boys and girls aged 8 and 9 there are. Encourage them to analyse and present results orally. See also Year 5 Block C.

Activity ④

Prior learning
Children can recall the relationships between kilometres/metres, metres/centimetres, kilograms/grams, litres/millilitres. They can choose and use appropriate units to estimate, measure and record length and weight.

Framework objective
Choose and use standard metric units and their abbreviations when estimating, measuring and recording length, weight and capacity; know the meaning of 'kilo', 'centi' and 'milli' and, where appropriate, use decimal notation to record measurements (for example, 1.3m or 0.6kg)

Vocabulary
metric unit, standard unit, millimetre (mm), centimetre (cm), metre (m), kilogram (kg), gram (g), litre (l), millilitre (ml)

Resources
Interactive activity: Measurement dilemmas
Worksheets: Measurement dilemmas (1) and (2)

④ Measurement dilemmas

Display the first screen of the interactive activity 'Measurement dilemmas'. Ask the children to work with a partner to decide which unit of measurement they would use to measure each item. Tell them to move the labels into the correct positions and explain their choices. They repeat the activity on screen 2, but this time they first need to estimate the measurement and then select the correct label from the options provided at the foot of the screen.

Teacher support
Less confident learners: Ask children to work in groups with adult support.
More confident learners: Ask children to measure classroom objects, choosing appropriate tools. They should record in metres, centimetres and millimetres.

Common misconception
Children do not know the relationships between units of length.
With the children, create and display a chart that shows relationships between units of length. Regularly ask the children questions that encourage them to use the chart.

Probing questions
● Which is a good estimate for the length of this window: 1.5m, 150mm, or 15cm?

BLOCK C

● Is it possible to measure a curved line? How would you go about it?

Next steps
Support: Ask these children to complete the worksheet 'Measurement dilemmas (1)'. See also Year 3 Block D Unit 2.
Extension: Ask these children to complete the worksheet 'Measurement dilemmas (2)'. See also Year 4 Block D Unit 2.

Activity ⑤

Prior learning
Children can recall the relationships between km/m, m/cm, kg/g, l/ml. They can measure and draw to a suitable degree of accuracy (for example, measure length to the nearest half centimetre).

Framework objective
Interpret intervals and divisions on partially numbered scales and record readings accurately, where appropriate to the nearest tenth of a unit

Vocabulary
metric unit, standard unit, millimetre (mm), centimetre (cm), metre (m), kilogram (kg), gram (g), litre (l), millilitre (ml)

Resources
Display page: Counting stick
Resource sheet: Self-assessment
Classroom resources: 1 metre counting stick (marked into ten sections), whiteboards and pens

⑤ What's my line?

Reveal the display page 'Counting stick'. Explain that the illustration represents a counting stick that is one metre long. Ask the children to record this in centimetres on their whiteboards. Point to a division on the stick (for example, the fourth mark) and ask the children to record the measurement in metres (0.4 metres). Point halfway between the fourth and fifth mark and ask the children to record again, in centimetres. Repeat for other divisions. Invite individuals to explain how they work out a measurement. Decide whether to use the self-assessment sheet for the children to record their achievements and next steps.

Teacher support
Less confident learners: Mark 50cm on the stick as a guide for these children.
More confident learners: Ask children to convert each measurement to metres.

Common misconception
Children do not understand that each division = 10 centimetres = 0.1 metres.
Give children an outline of a counting stick to fill in with cm and metric equivalents.

Probing questions
● Point to 40cm on this stick. How did you know that that is the correct place?
● Look at this point just past halfway. How could you record that in centimetres? How many millimetres would that be?

Next steps
Support: Ask the children to work in pairs, taking turns to ask each other to show 0.6 (and so on) on the counting stick and tell their partner its centimetre equivalent. See also Year 3 Block D Unit 3.
Extension: Ask the children to work in pairs with a counting stick. They should take it in turns to estimate measurements between each division (for example, 0.42 metres), and convert them to centimetres. See also Year 4 Block D Unit 2.

BLOCK C

Activity ⑥

Prior learning Children can count in twos, fives and tens and continue a given sequence of numbers.	**Framework objective** Compare the impact of representations where scales have intervals of differing step size **Vocabulary** graph, chart, table, diagram, horizontal axis, vertical axis, axes, label, title, scale, interval, pictogram, bar chart, tally chart, greatest/least value **Resources** **Interactive activity (ITP):** Data handling **Worksheets:** Data handling problems (1) and (2) **Resource sheet:** Self-assessment

⑥ Data handling problems

Open the ITP 'Data handling'. Select the data on pets. Hide the colours, and then select a vertical bar chart. Ask: *What does each division represent? From the data, which colour represents mice/dogs? How did you work it out? What was the least/most popular pet?* Next, change the data to population, hide totals, reveal colours and select horizontal bar chart. Ask: *What is the scale of this graph? How many people are between 21 and 50 years old? What is the least common age group? Why was a different scale used for each graph?* Share ideas. Decide whether to use the self-assessment sheet for the children to record their achievements and next steps.

Teacher support
Less confident learners: Let these children work in pairs, with adult support.
More confident learners: Encourage these children to use the ITP to explore other data and compare the scales. Invite them to think of questions to ask a partner about the graph, if one set of data was hidden.

Common misconception
Children do not recognise that one step on the scale may stand for different quantities.
Display a bar chart, using the 'Data handling' ITP. Demonstrate what happens when the scale is changed (for example, 1 step = 2/20/100). Ask the children to work out the values shown by each bar after each change.

Probing questions
● How can you tell that this bar shows the number of young people in the village?
● What is the scale on this graph? How is it different from the last graph? Why do you think a different scale was used for this graph?

Next steps
Support: Ask small groups to complete the worksheet 'Data handling problems (1)'. Ask: *What is the number of people when the symbol = 20? What is the number when the symbol = 10? How many symbols would be needed if the results were to stay the same?* See also Year 3 Block C Unit 3.
Extension: Ask small groups to complete the worksheet 'Data handling problems (2)'. Ask: *What is the number of people when the symbol = 20? What is the number when the symbol = 10/5? What difference does this make to the results? If you wanted the results to be the same, how many of each symbol would you need each time?* See also Year 4 Block C Unit 3.

BLOCK C

Unit 3 🔲 Handling data and measures

Introduction

In this unit children continue to handle data. They collect, organise, present and interpret data to answer related questions, identifying further questions. They construct tables, pictogram diagrams, tally charts and bar charts, explaining reasoning using text, diagrams and graphs. Children read from scales, comparing the impact of different scales. They use standard metric units to estimate, measure and record measurements.

Framework objectives	Assessment focuses		Success criteria for Year 4	Learning outcomes
	Level 4	Level 3		
① Gathering information ② Presenting results ③ Final report ④ Bedtimes				
Suggest a line of enquiry and the strategy needed to follow it; collect, organise and interpret selected information to find answers	• develop own strategies for solving problems, e.g. • make their own suggestions of ways to tackle a range of problems • make connections to previous work • pose and answer questions related to a problem • check answers and ensure solutions make sense in the context of the problem • review their work and approaches	• select the mathematics they use in a wider range of classroom activities, e.g. • use classroom discussions to break into a problem • put the problem into their own words • choose their own equipment appropriate to the task, including calculators • try different approaches and find ways of overcoming difficulties that arise when they are solving problems	• thinks about and discusses how to collect information that is relevant to the problem or question posed • decides what form of presentation is appropriate after considering options	*I can think about an investigation, predict what might happen and decide how I might find information by doing a survey or taking measurements.*
Answer a question by identifying what data to collect; organise, present, analyse and interpret the data in tables, diagrams, tally charts, pictograms and bar charts, using ICT where appropriate	• collect discrete data, e.g. • given a problem, suggest possible answers and data to collect • record discrete data using a frequency table • represent collected data in frequency diagrams, e.g. • suggest an appropriate frequency diagram to represent particular data, e.g. decide whether a bar chart, Venn diagram or pictogram would be most appropriate and for pictograms use one symbol to represent, say, 2, 5, 10 or 100 • continue to use Venn and Carroll diagrams to record their sorting and classifying of information	• gather information, e.g. • decide what data to collect to answer a question, e.g. what is the most common way to travel to school • make appropriate choices for recording data, e.g. a tally chart or frequency table • construct bar charts and pictograms, where the symbol represents a group of units • use Venn and Carroll diagrams to record their sorting and classifying of information	• knows what information needs to be collected and can decide how to record results of a survey, e.g. in the form of tally chart or frequency chart • is able to present this information in the form of a block graph, pictogram or bar chart	*I can collect data in different ways and decide whether to put it in a table, diagram, tally chart, pictogram or bar chart so that it is easy to understand.*
Report solutions to puzzles and problems, giving explanations and reasoning orally and in writing, using diagrams and symbols	• present information and results in a clear and organised way, e.g. • organise written work, e.g. record results in order • begin to work in an organised way from the start • consider appropriate units • use related vocabulary accurately	• discuss their mathematical work and begin to explain their thinking, e.g. • use appropriate mathematical vocabulary • talk about their findings by referring to their written work • use and interpret mathematical symbols and diagrams	• presents information and results orally and in writing, using diagrams and symbols	*I can tell people what I have found out and show some graphs to back up my conclusions.*

Unit 3 📖 Handling data and measures

Framework objectives	Assessment focuses		Success criteria for Year 4	Learning outcomes
	Level 4	Level 3		
(5) How much does it hold?				
Choose and use standard metric units and their abbreviations when estimating, measuring and recording length, weight and capacity; know the meaning of 'kilo', 'centi' and 'milli' and, where appropriate, use decimal notation to record measurements (e.g. 1.3m or 0.6kg)	• choose and use appropriate units and instruments • interpret, with appropriate accuracy, numbers on a range of measuring instruments, e.g. • measure a length using mm, to within 2mm	• use non-standard units and standard metric units of length, capacity and mass in a range of contexts, e.g. • measure a length to the nearest ½cm	• estimates capacity of different-sized containers • orders objects according to their capacity	*I can estimate the length of a line in centimetres and millimetres and then measure the line to see how close my estimate was.*
(6) Scale solution				
Interpret intervals and divisions on partially numbered scales and record readings accurately, where appropriate to the nearest tenth of a unit	• interpret, with appropriate accuracy, numbers on a range of measuring instruments	• use non-standard units and standard metric units of length, capacity and mass in a range of contexts, e.g. • read simple scales, e.g. increments of 2, 5 or 10	• can read and interpret different scales on measuring instruments and graphs	*I can use different kinds of rulers and measuring tapes to measure lengths accurately.*
Compare the impact of representations where scales have intervals of differing step size	• interpret frequency diagrams, e.g. • interpret the scale on bar graphs and line graphs, reading between the labelled divisions, e.g. reading 17 on a scale labelled in fives • interpret the total amount of data represented • represent collected data in frequency diagrams • suggest an appropriate frequency diagram to represent particular data, e.g. decide whether a bar chart, Venn diagram or pictogram would be most appropriate and for pictograms use one symbol to represent, say, 2, 5, 10 or 100 • construct simple line graphs, e.g. • decide upon an appropriate scale for a graph, e.g. labelled divisions representing 2, 5, 10, 100	• extract and interpret information presented in simple tables, lists, bar charts and pictograms, e.g. • read scales labelled in twos, fives and tens, including reading between labelled divisions such as a point halfway between 40 and 50 or 8 and 10 • construct bar charts and pictograms, where the symbol represents a group of units, e.g. • decide upon an appropriate scale for a graph, e.g. labelled divisions of 2, or, for a pictogram, one symbol to represent 2 or 5	• can interpret different scales used on measuring instruments and graphs • can explain why a given scale is useful	*I can compare graphs with different scales and decide which is the most useful.*

BLOCK C

Activities ① – ④

Prior learning
Children can consider a question and develop a response by referring to relevant data. They can make and use lists, tables and simple bar charts to organise and interpret the information. They can use Venn diagrams or Carroll diagrams to sort data and objects using more than one criterion.

Framework objectives
● Suggest a line of enquiry and the strategy needed to follow it; collect, organise and interpret selected information to find answers
● **Answer a question by identifying what data to collect; organise, present, analyse and interpret the data in tables, diagrams, tally charts, pictograms and bar charts, using ICT where appropriate**
● Report solutions to puzzles and problems, giving explanations and reasoning orally and in writing, using diagrams and symbols

Vocabulary
problem, solution, explain, reasoning, reason, predict, classify, represent, interpret, data, information, survey, questionnaire, graph, chart, table, diagram, horizontal axis, vertical axis, axes, label, title, scale, interval, pictogram, bar chart, tally chart, greatest/least value

Resources
Resource sheets: Self-assessment, Tally chart, Frequency chart, Block graph template, Bar chart template, Pictogram template
Classroom resources: sticky notes

① Gathering information

Ask the children to recall what they do when they get home from school each evening (Monday to Friday). Divide them into groups and ask them to record the activities they have carried out during the previous five school evenings (there can be more than one activity for each child). Challenge them to present the information they have collected in the form of a frequency chart or tally chart. When they have done this, decide whether to use the self-assessment sheet for the children to record their achievements and what they need to do next.

Teacher support
Less confident learners: Ensure that less confident learners are working with adult support and/or give them the resource sheets 'Frequency chart' or 'Tally chart' to assist them in gathering the information.
More confident learners: Encourage these children to make suggestions for collecting and organising the information and to support others: to distribute tasks and check progress.

Common misconception
Children have difficulty deciding what to include in the enquiry.
Ensure that there is some whole-class discussion before groups are asked to work independently. Help the children to agree on what needs to be included.

Probing questions
● How many different activities do you do? What are they? Do you do different activities on different evenings (for example, swimming, dancing, playing outside), or do you always do the same (homework, watch TV, have tea)?
● What is the best way to record all this information?

Next steps
Support: Ask the children to practise tallying by asking pairs to carry out an activity in one minute (for example, writing their whole name). One child writes their name and the other child keeps a tally of how many times it is done. Then they swap over. See also Year 4 Block C Units 1 and 2.
Extension: Ask the children to devise a questionnaire to collect information to compare after-school activities in summer and in winter. See also Year 5 Block C.

② **Presenting results**

The children should work with the same group as in the previous activity and with the same information. Ask the whole class to share the information they collected in the previous activity, and calculate a total for the whole class for each activity collected. Invite each group to present the class results as a pictogram, a bar chart and a block graph. They should share tasks amongst the group. Ask groups to decide what scales are appropriate for their graphs and charts or suggest that they experiment with different step sizes to see how it alters the appearance of the graphs and their perceptions of variations. When they have completed this, decide whether to use the self-assessment sheet for the children to record their achievements and what they need to do next.

Teacher support
Less confident learners: Provide these children with copies of the resource sheets 'Block graph template', 'Bar chart template' and 'Pictogram template'.
More confident learners: Ask these children to experiment with a greater variety of scales on their charts.

Common misconception
Children lack confidence in using different scales on graphs and charts.
Provide opportunities for children to look at examples on a variety of computer programs, as well as the interactive activity 'Data handling'.

Probing questions
● What ways can you choose from to present the data?
● What makes the information difficult or easy to interpret?

Next steps
Support: Ask the children to explore examples of bar charts and pictograms with different scales on computer programs. See also Year 3 Block C.
Extension: Let these children use computer programs to create bar charts and pictograms with different scales. See also Year 5 Block C.

③ **Final report**

Invite the groups to report back to the whole class on their findings by showing their graphs and charts and commenting on the processes of collecting and producing their data and of drawing conclusions from it. Once all the groups have presented their reports, decide whether to use the self-assessment sheet for the children to record their achievements and what they need to do next.

Teacher support
Less confident learners: Ask these children to discuss their findings with an adult before presenting them to the rest of the class.
More confident learners: Encourage these children to identify ways of refining the enquiry.

Common misconception
Having produced data in the form of graphs and charts, children may have difficulty reporting their findings.
Ask children to devise questions that can be asked about the information in the graphs and charts. Then ask them to answer the questions themselves, and so turn these answers into a report on their findings.

Probing questions
● What have you found out?
● Are your results what you expected?
● What evidence do you have to support your conclusions?

Next steps
Support: Ask these children to work together on interpreting given data and presenting explanations. See also Year 3 Block C Unit 3.
Extension: Challenge these children to suggest what they could do differently if they were to carry out the investigation again. See also Year 5 Block C.

④ Bedtimes

Provide each child with a sticky note. Ask them to write down on it what time they usually go to bed and also their age and name. When they have done this, collect all the sticky notes. Draw a large Carroll diagram on the board. Ask: *Do you think more children go to bed before 8pm or at 8pm or after?* Write headings on the Carroll diagram: 'before 8pm', 'at 8pm or after', 'eight-year-olds' and 'nine-year-olds'. In turn, invite the children to place the sticky notes on the diagram. Invite them to draw conclusions from the activity, and then to present the results in another form. When they have completed this activity, decide whether to use the self-assessment sheet for the children to record their achievements and what they need to do next.

Teacher support
Less confident learners: Discuss with the children what would be an appropriate way to make a permanent record of the findings.
More confident learners: Encourage these children to experiment with different ways of reporting the findings.

Common misconception
Having recorded the findings on the board, children may be unsure how to proceed.
Ask children to sketch graphs and charts before they commit to drawing a particular type and scale.

Probing questions
● Should we put results for eight-year-olds and nine-year-olds on the same graph/pictogram/bar chart?
● Can we refine or improve on the enquiry?

Next steps
Support: Ask the children to work in pairs or small groups to split the data further into boys and girls. See also Year 3 Block C Unit 3.
Extension: Challenge these children to divide the data into boys and girls and produce the required graph, chart or pictogram. See also Year 5 Block C.

Activity ⑤

Prior learning
Children can recall the relationships between kilometres and metres, metres and centimetres, kilograms and grams, litres and millilitres. They can choose and use appropriate units to estimate, measure and record length and weight.

Framework objective
Choose and use standard metric units and their abbreviations when estimating, measuring and recording length, weight and capacity; know the meaning of 'kilo', 'centi' and 'milli' and, where appropriate, use decimal notation to record measurements (for example, 1.3m or 0.6kg)

Vocabulary
metric unit, standard unit, millimetre (mm), centimetre (cm), metre (m), kilogram (kg), gram (g), litre (l), millilitre (ml)

Resources
Interactive activity: How much does it hold?

⑤ How much does it hold?

Display the interactive activity 'How much does it hold?'. Ask the children to work in pairs to match the capacity labels on the first screen to the objects shown. Then choose different children to move the labels to the appropriate containers and explain their choices. Ask: *What problems did you have when you were trying to decide the most appropriate label?* (For example, they are in different units.) For screen 2, ask the children to move the number labels to order the containers by which holds the most. Again, encourage them to explain their decisions.

Teacher support
Less confident learners: Provide the children with a litre/millilitres conversion table to help with their calculations.
More confident learners: Ask these children to find different-sized containers in the classroom and estimate, then measure, their capacity in litres/millilitres.

Common misconception
Children have difficulty converting litres to millilitres.
Encourage children to create their own charts showing conversions from litres to millilitres (for example 3 litres = 3000 millilitres, ½ litre = 500 millilitres), which they can refer to in the future and eventually learn.

Probing questions
● Tell me another way to write 7 litres.
● Is the capacity of a vinegar bottle likely to be 0.3 litres or 3 litres?

Next steps
Support: Give these children three different-sized grocery items that are measured in litres. Ask them to work in pairs to put them in order of size and to convert the capacities to millilitres. See also Year 3 Block D Unit 1.
Extension: Give these children several different-sized grocery items that are measured in litres/millilitres. Ask them to convert them to one unit and put them in order of size. See also Year 4 Block D Unit 1.

Activity ⑥

Prior learning
Children can recall the relationships between kilometres and metres, metres and centimetres, kilograms and grams, litres and millilitres. They can measure and draw to a suitable degree of accuracy (for example, measure length to the nearest half centimetre and weight to the nearest half division on the scales).

Framework objectives
● Interpret intervals and divisions on partially numbered scales and record readings accurately, where appropriate to the nearest tenth of a unit
● Compare the impact of representations where scales have intervals of differing step size

Vocabulary
metric unit, standard unit, millimetre (mm), centimetre (cm), metre (m), kilogram (kg), gram (g), litre (l), millilitre (ml), axis, bar chart, scale, interval, greatest/least value

Resources
Interactive activity: Scale solution

⑥ Scale solution

Display the interactive activity 'Scale solution'. Show screen 1. Ask the children to work in pairs to find the scale for each jug. Can they also work out how much liquid is in each jug? When they have done this, choose a pair to drag the arrows to join each measurement to the correct jug. Encourage them to explain to the class how they worked out each one. Repeat for screens 2 and 3, asking appropriate questions on reading weighing scales and interpreting scales on a bar chart.

Teacher support
Less confident learners: Let these children work in small groups with adult support.
More confident learners: Ask these children to work in pairs to create different scales for the jugs, weighing scales or bar charts, and to calculate the quantities for each one.

Common misconception
Children do not check the scale or key before interpreting a bar chart or a pictogram.
Ask children to write a list of questions that they should ask themselves when looking at a bar chart or pictogram for the first time. For example: *What is the chart about? What is the scale? What is the key?* and so on.

Probing questions
● How did you work out the scale for these jugs? What helped you?
● What is the scale used on this bar chart? Why do think this is appropriate for this topic? How does it help you when interpreting the graph?

Next steps
Support: Provide some appropriate data, and ask the children to work in pairs to draw three bar charts to represent the data – each bar chart must have a different scale. See also Year 4 Block C Unit 2.
Extension: Ask these children to draw their own capacity scales with labelled arrows pointing at different amounts. They should then challenge a partner to write the amounts shown by the arrows. See also Year 5 Block C Unit 1.

BLOCK C

Units 1, 2 & 3 📖 Periodic assessment

These activities can be used at any time during the teaching of this block to assess those children that you think have achieved the objective. A grid highlighting the related assessment focuses and expected learning outcomes for each activity can be found on the CD-ROM.

Collecting and presenting data

Framework objective
Answer a question by identifying what data to collect; organise, present, analyse and interpret the data

Learning outcomes
● I can collect data and put it in a table to help me explore an idea and find out more about it.
● I can tell people what I have found out and show some graphs to back up my conclusions.

Part 1
Ask the children to work in pairs. They should work through part 1 of the worksheet 'Collecting and presenting data' together.

Part 2
Before the children begin part 2 of the worksheet 'Collecting and presenting data', discuss what data is relevant at the time the activity is carried out. This may link with cross-curricular work or be a survey of the children's own choice (for example, favourite colours). Ask them to discuss how they will go about collecting and presenting information. Pairs of children should work without adult intervention in order for you to assess their independent skills.

Venn diagrams and Carroll diagrams

Framework objective
Report solutions to problems, giving explanations and reasoning orally and in writing, using diagrams and symbols

Learning outcome
● I can explain how I solved a puzzle using a diagram to help me.

Ask the children to work independently on the tasks in parts 1 and 2 of the worksheet 'Venn diagrams and Carroll diagrams'. They will need the resource sheet 'Venn diagram template'. Next, ask the children to work independently on part 3. Provide them with copies of the resource sheet 'Carroll diagram template'. Finally, ask the children to answer the questions in part 4 of the worksheet and discuss their findings with others as described.

Units of measurement

Framework objective
Choose and use standard metric units; know the meaning of 'kilo', 'centi' and 'milli' and, where appropriate, use decimal notation to record measurements

Learning outcomes
● I can estimate and measure lengths, weights, and mass to help me find out more about a question I am exploring.
● I can order containers according to which will hold the most.
● I can estimate and measure the capacity in litres and millilitres.
● I know the relationships between units of weight.

Ask the children to complete the worksheet 'Units of measurement'. Choose individual children to explain how they decided which was the best unit of measurement to use. What did they look at when trying to measure accurately? Can anyone explain a rule for converting metres to centimetres?

Name   Date

Collecting and presenting data

Part 1: Watching birds

Two children collected data on how many birds they saw in their gardens in one week. These were their results:

Type of bird	Number of this type of bird
robin	14
blackbird	10
blue tit	12
sparrow	8
thrush	4
wagtail	6

The children then wanted to draw a bar graph to show the information. Using the information from the table above, help them to complete the graph below.

A graph to show how many birds we saw in our gardens in one week

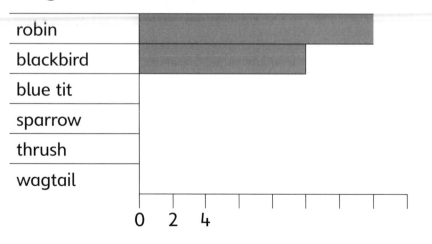

Name	Date

(continued)

Part 2: Collecting, presenting and reporting data

You are going to collect, present and report some data of your own.
Work with a partner. Discuss with your teacher what data you need to
collect for this task.

1. Decide what method of collecting data you will use, for example a
tally chart.

2. When you have collected your data, discuss with your partner how you
want to present the information (for example, pictogram, bar chart
or block graph).

3. Decide whether to use a computer program.

4. Present your findings and explain them to others in your class.

_____

_____

_____

_____

_____

_____

_____

_____

_____

How easy?

Red

Amber

Green

How do you think you have done?

_____

_____

Name   Date

Venn diagrams and Carroll diagrams

Write down all the numbers from 1 to 30.

Part 1

◼ Use a Venn diagram to sort the numbers 1 to 30 according to these criteria.

Odd numbers _____

Multiples of 5_____

Multiples of 5 and odd numbers _____

Which numbers will be placed outside the circles? _____

_____

Part 2

◼ Use a second Venn diagram to sort the numbers 1 to 30 according to these criteria.

Even numbers _____

Multiples of 3 _____

Multiples of 3 and even numbers _____

Which numbers will be placed outside the circles? _____

Part 3

◼ Now use Carroll diagrams to sort the numbers 1 to 30 according to these criteria.

1. odd and even; multiples of 6 and not multiples of 6

2. odd and even; multiples of 7 and not multiples of 7

3. odd and even; multiples of 9 and not multiples of 9

Name	Date

(continued)

Part 4

Answer these questions and then report back to your teacher, to a partner or to the rest of the class.

1. What do you notice about multiples of 6?

_____

2. Can you predict what you would find out about multiples of 4 and multiples of 8 if you did the same investigation?

_____

3. What about multiples of 10?

_____

4. Can you draw a conclusion about multiples of even numbers?

_____

5. Can you draw a conclusion about multiples of odd numbers?

_____

_____

_____

_____

_____

_____

_____

How easy?

Red

Amber

Green

How do you think you have done?

_____

_____

Name   Date

Units of measurement

1. Measure these lines in centimetres:

a) _____

Answer: _____

b) _____

Answer: _____

2. Draw lines of these lengths:

a) 57 mm

b) 162 mm

3. What unit would you use to measure:

a) the height of a mountain _____

b) the depth of a ruler _____

4. What unit would you use to find:

a) the capacity of a watering can _____

b) the weight of a bag of potatoes _____

4. Find the equivalent unit of measurement:

cm	1.25 metres
450 grams	kg
ml	3.75 litres
42mm	metres

How easy?

Red
Amber
Green

How do you think you have done?

_____

_____

BLOCK D

Calculating, measuring and understanding shape

Expected prior learning

Check that children can already:
- recall the relationships between kilometres and metres, metres and centimetres, kilograms and grams, litres and millilitres
- read, to the nearest division and half division, scales that are numbered or partially numbered
- read the time on a 12-hour digital clock and to the nearest five minutes on an analogue clock; calculate time intervals and find start or end times for a given time interval
- use a set-square to draw right angles and to identify right angles in 2D shapes; compare angles with a right angle; recognise that a straight line is equivalent to two right angles
- use four compass directions to describe direction (N, S, E, W).

Objectives overview

The text in this diagram identifies the focus of mathematics learning within the block.

Key aspects of learning
- Information processing
- Communication

Solving one- and two-step word problems involving numbers, money, measures or time

Standard metric units

Reading from partly numbered scales

Am, pm, 12-hour clock and time intervals

Areas and perimeters of rectangles

Angles in degrees; compass points

Horizontal and vertical; position on a grid

BLOCK D: Calculating, measuring and understanding shape

Addition and subtraction

Mental methods: pairs of two-digit numbers

Written methods: two- and three-digit numbers, £. p

Multiplication and division

Tables to 10 × 10; multiplying by 10 or 100, two-digit doubles

Written methods: multipling and dividing TU by U; rounding remainders

Using a calculator

BLOCK D

Unit 1 📖 Calculating, measuring and understanding shape

Introduction
In this unit children develop mental methods of calculating addition or difference of pairs of two-digit numbers. They use simple coordinates and compass points to plot positions. Measures work concentrates on mass and reading from scales. They read from both digital and analogue clocks and to the nearest minute. Problem solving is an integral part of this unit and speaking and listening skills are developed as children listen to each other and take notes.

Framework objectives	Assessment focuses		Success criteria for Year 4	Learning outcomes
	Level 4	**Level 3**		
① Spell saucery				
Solve one-step and two-step problems involving numbers, money or measures, including time; choose and carry out appropriate calculations, using calculator methods where appropriate	• develop own strategies for solving problems • solve problems with or without a calculator, e.g. • solve two-step problems, choosing appropriate operations • deal with two constraints simultaneously • interpret a calculator display of 4.5 as £4.50 in context of money • carry out simple calculations involving negative numbers in context • check the reasonableness of results with reference to the context or size of numbers	• try different approaches and find ways of overcoming difficulties that arise when they are solving problems, e.g. • check their work and make appropriate corrections, e.g. decide that two numbers less than 100 cannot give a total more than 200 and correct the addition • begin to look for patterns in results as they work and use them to find other possible outcomes • use mental recall of addition and subtraction facts to 20 in solving problems involving larger numbers	• can solve problems using mass • can choose what calculation is needed to solve a problem • can decide whether it is appropriate to use a calculator	*I can work out how to solve problems with one or two steps.* *I can solve problems using measurements.* *I can choose what calculation to work out and I can decide whether a calculator will help me.*
② Adding and subtracting mentally				
Add or subtract mentally pairs of two-digit whole numbers (e.g. 47 + 58, 91 − 35)	• use a range of mental methods of computation with addition and subtraction	• add and subtract two-digit numbers mentally, e.g. • calculate 36 + 19, 63 − 26	• uses different strategies to add and subtract pairs of two-digit numbers mentally	*I can use mental addition and subtraction to help me solve problems.*
③ Pond life				
Recognise horizontal and vertical lines; use the eight compass points to describe direction; describe and identify the position of a square on a grid of squares	• use the properties of 2D and 3D shapes, e.g. • use mathematical terms such as horizontal, vertical	• describe position and movement, e.g. • use terms to give direction along a route	• can describe the position of a square on a grid of squares • knows which lines are horizontal or vertical	*I know when a line is horizontal or vertical.* *I can describe the position of a square on a grid of squares.*

BLOCK D

Unit 1 📖 Calculating, measuring and understanding shape

Framework objectives	Assessment focuses		Success criteria for Year 4	Learning outcomes
	Level 4	Level 3		
④ Mass - make your mind up!				
Choose and use standard metric units and their abbreviations when estimating, measuring and recording length, weight and capacity; know the meaning of 'kilo', 'centi' and 'milli' and, where appropriate, use decimal notation to record measurements (e.g. 1.3m or 0.6kg)	• choose and use appropriate units and instruments • interpret, with appropriate accuracy, numbers on a range of measuring instruments	• use non-standard units and standard metric units of length, capacity and mass in a range of contexts	• can use units of weight to measure mass • knows the relationships between units of weight	*I can estimate and measure a weight.* *I know the relationships between units of weight.* *I can write a mass in kilograms using a decimal point.*
⑤ Weighing scales				
Interpret intervals and divisions on partially numbered scales and record readings accurately, where appropriate to the nearest tenth of a unit	• interpret, with appropriate accuracy, numbers on a range of measuring instruments	• use non-standard units and standard metric units of mass in a range of contexts, e.g. • read simple scales, e.g. increments of 2, 5 or 10	• can read a weight in grams or kilograms from a scale marked in kilograms	*I can use kitchen or bathroom scale to measure a weight.* *I can read a weight in kilograms and grams from a scale marked in kg.*
⑥ Clocks				
Read time to the nearest minute; use am, pm and 12-hour clock notation; choose units of time to measure time intervals; calculate time intervals from clocks and timetables	• use units of time, e.g. • calculate time durations that go over the hour	• use standard units of time, e.g. • read a 12-hour clock and generally calculate time durations that do not go over the hour	• can tell the time to the nearest minute, using am and pm • can work out how long an event takes	*I can tell the time to the minute on a clock with hands.* *I can write down a time using am and pm. I can work out how long something takes if I know the start and end times.*

Activity ①

Prior learning
Children can identify the calculation needed to solve a word problem. They explain and record their methods and solutions to problems and calculations.

Framework objective
Solve one-step and two-step problems involving numbers, money or measures, including time; choose and carry out appropriate calculations, using calculator methods where appropriate

Vocabulary
problem, solution, answer, method, explain, predict, reason, reasoning, calculation, add, subtract, multiply, divide, mass, weight, kilogram (kg), gram (g)

Resources
Worksheets: Spell saucery (1), (2) and (3)
Classroom resources: calculators (one per child)

① Spell saucery

Ask the children to complete the worksheet 'Spell saucery (1)'. Allow them to use calculators. When they have completed the activity, invite individuals to share their spells. How many different spells did the class create? Why was it possible to create such a variety?

Teacher support
Less confident learners: Ask these children to work in pairs with adult support.
More confident learners: Ask these children to change the weights of the items and then challenge a partner to create a spell.

Common misconception
Children do not know which calculation or operation to use.
Ask children to work in small groups to write a number sentence for each part of a word problem, prior to calculating. Discuss how children choose which operation to use.

Probing questions
● Explain what you did to get your answer.
● How did you know what operation(s) to use?
● Could you have done it in a different way?
● Did you use a calculator? Why/why not?

Next steps
Support: Provide these children with the worksheet 'Spell saucery (2)' and ask them to complete it. Encourage them to write a number sentence for each part of the problem before calculating. See also Year 4 Block A Unit 3.
Extension: Ask these children to complete the worksheet 'Spell saucery (3)'. See also Year 4 Block D Unit 2.

Activity ②

Children can recall addition and subtraction facts for each number to 20. They can add or subtract mentally combinations of one-digit and two-digit numbers.

Framework objective
Add or subtract mentally pairs of two-digit whole numbers (for example, 47 + 58, 91 – 35)

Vocabulary
calculate, calculation, answer, method, explain, relationship, partition, digit, add, subtract, sum, total, difference, plus, minus

Resources
Display page: Adding and subtracting mentally
Worksheets: Adding and subtracting mentally (1), (2), (3), (4) and (5)
Resource sheet: Self-assessment
Classroom resources: whiteboards and pens

② Adding and subtracting mentally

Reveal the display page 'Adding and subtracting mentally'. Go through the number sentences one at a time. Ask the children to mentally calculate each answer, write it on their whiteboards and hold them up when you say *Show me*. After they have shown their answers, ask different children to explain their strategies. Once they have done this, decide whether to use the self-assessment sheet for the children to record their achievements and what they need to do next.

Teacher support
Less confident learners: If necessary, provide these children with place value arrow cards (tens and units) to enable them to make up each number, prior to calculations.
More confident learners: Give these children sets of three numbers to add mentally.

Common misconception
Children lack recall of key number facts.
Provide regular practice of a range of key number facts through games, quizzes and so on.

Probing questions
● What strategies could you use to help you work out 71 – 26? Did anyone use a different method?
● Why do 23 + 35, 33 + 25 and 53 + 5 all give the same answer?

Next steps
Support: Ask the children to complete the worksheet 'Adding and subtracting mentally (1)' or 'Adding and subtracting mentally (2)'. See also Year 4 Block A Unit 3.
Extension: Invite these children to play the addition game provided on the worksheets 'Adding and subtracting mentally (3), (4) and (5)'. See also Year 5 Block D Unit 1.

 BLOCK D

Activity ③

Prior learning Children can use four compass directions to describe direction (N, S, E, W).	**Framework objective** Recognise horizontal and vertical lines; use the eight compass points to describe direction; describe and identify the position of a square on a grid of squares **Vocabulary** position, direction, north-east (NE), north-west (NW), south-west (SW), south-east (SE), clockwise, anticlockwise, horizontal, vertical, grid **Resources** **Worksheets:** Pond life (1) and (2) **Classroom resources:** whiteboards and pens

③ Pond life

Provide each child with a copy of the worksheet 'Pond life (1)'. Alternatively, display the worksheet on a whiteboard and ask the questions orally – tell the children that they can write their answers on their whiteboards. Discuss the different routes for each answer. Ask: *How many different routes could the blackbird use to eat all the insects?*

Teacher support
Less confident learners: Let these children work in pairs to answer the questions.
More confident learners: Ask these children to devise a route for one of the creatures shown on the grid on the worksheet, and then challenge a partner to tell them at which square they finish their route.

Common misconception
Children mix up west and east.
Show children that the two initials spell WE to help them remember which way round they appear.

Probing questions
● The blackbird moves 2 squares east and 3 squares south. Which square is he on?
● The fly moves west 4 squares and north 1 square. Where is he?
● The ladybird moves 2 squares north. On the grid, will her path be horizontal or vertical?

Next steps
Support: Provide further opportunities for the children to interpret grids and reinforce positional language. See also Year 3 Block D Unit 2.
Extension: Ask these children to carry out the activity on the worksheet 'Pond life (2)' in pairs. See also Year 4 Block D Unit 2.

BLOCK D

Activity ④

Prior learning
Children can recall the relationships between kilometres and metres, metres and centimetres, kilograms and grams, litres and millilitres.

Framework objective
Choose and use standard metric units and their abbreviations when estimating, measuring and recording length, weight and capacity; know the meaning of 'kilo', 'centi' and 'milli' and, where appropriate, use decimal notation to record measurements (for example, 1.3m or 0.6kg)

Vocabulary
measure, estimate, metric unit, standard unit, mass, weight, balance, scales, units of measurement and abbreviations: kilogram (kg), gram (g)

Resources
Interactive activity: Mass – make your mind up!
Worksheets: Mass – make your mind up! (1) and (2)

④ Mass – make your mind up!

Let the children work through the questions on the interactive activity 'Mass – make your mind up!'. Encourage them to explain their choices.

Teacher support
Less confident learners: Let these children work in pairs to answer the questions on the interactive activity.
More confident learners: Invite these children to use the questions on the screen as a model for them to create similar questions for a partner to solve.

Common misconception
Children do not understand the relationship between kilograms and grams.
Give children opportunities to practise matching the different ways of recording the same mass. For example, 3.6kg = 3600g.

Probing questions
● How did you know that that mass was more than this one?
● Would you rather have ¼kg chocolate or 350 grams? Why?

Next steps
Support: Ask these children to complete the worksheet 'Mass – make your mind up! (1)', to give them practice in ordering units of mass on a number line. See also Year 4 Block C Unit 3.
Extension: Ask these children to complete the worksheet 'Mass – make your mind up! (2)'. See also Year 4 Block D Unit 2.

BLOCK D

Activity ⑤

Prior learning
Children can recall the relationships between kilometres and metres, metres and centimetres, kilograms and grams, litres and millilitres. They are able to read, to the nearest division and half division, scales that are numbered or are partially numbered.

Framework objective
Interpret intervals and divisions on partially numbered scales and record readings accurately, where appropriate to the nearest tenth of a unit

Vocabulary
measure, estimate, metric unit, standard unit, mass, weight, balance, scales, units of measurement and abbreviations: kilogram (kg), gram (g)

Resources
Interactive activity: Weighing scales
Worksheet: Weighing scales
Resource sheet: Self-assessment
Classroom resources: whiteboards and pens

⑤ Weighing scales

Display the interactive activity 'Weighing scales'. Drag one of the items onto the scales. Ask the children to record its mass in decimals on their whiteboards. Turn on the digital readout to check their answers. Choose a child to explain their answer. Next, drag another item onto the scales, to join the first one. Ask questions such as: *What is the total weight? What is the difference in weight? How much do the items weigh in kg/g? How many bags of flour weigh 2kg?* When you have completed this activity, decide whether to use the self-assessment sheet for the children to record their achievements and next steps.

Teacher support
Less confident learners: Let these children work in small groups with an adult.
More confident learners: Ask these children to work in pairs, experimenting with weighing different combinations of items, each time working out the sum of items and difference in weights.

Common misconception
Children have difficulty converting weights in kilograms and grams to kilograms only.
Ask a child to say a mass in kilograms and grams and use place value arrow cards to show it as a decimal. For example, for 4kg 200g, children keep the 4 as it is a whole number of kilograms, but swap the 200 for 0.2 as 200 is two-tenths of a kilogram.

Probing questions
● How do you work out the difference in weight between these two items?
● This object weighs 150g. How many will I need to make 600g? How do you know?

Next steps
Support: Let these children work in small groups with adult support. They should take it in turns to weigh items and read masses off the scale. See also Year 4 Block C Unit 3.
Extension: Ask the children to work in pairs to complete the worksheet 'Weighing scales'. They could also estimate and then weigh each item using scales. See also Year 4 Block D Unit 2.

BLOCK D

Activity ⑥

Prior learning
Children can read the time on a 12-hour digital clock and to the nearest five minutes on an analogue clock. They can calculate time intervals and find start or end times for a given time interval.

Framework objective
Read time to the nearest minute; use am, pm and 12-hour clock notation; choose units of time to measure time intervals; calculate time intervals from clocks and timetables

Vocabulary
time, am, pm, digital, analogue, timetable, arrive, depart, hour (h), minute (min), second (s)

Resources
Interactive activity: Clocks
Resource sheets: Self-assessment, Clocks
Classroom resources: model analogue clocks (one per child), whiteboards and pens

⑥ Clocks

Display the analogue clock on the interactive activity 'Clocks'. Click 'randomise'. Ask the children to write the time in digital form on their whiteboards. Repeat several times. Next, click on the tab on the left-hand side of the screen to reveal the digital clock. Click 'randomise'. Say: *Show the same time on your analogue clocks.* Ask questions about intervals of time. For example: *I start walking home at this time* [point to clock] *and get home 50 minutes later. What time will it be?* or *I begin a journey at 11.45am and arrive at 2.10pm. How long was I travelling?* Decide whether to use the self-assessment sheet for the children to record their achievements and what they need to do next.

Teacher support
Less confident learners: Ask these children to work in small groups. Ask them similar questions, but randomise to five-minute intervals.
More confident learners: Let these children work in pairs. They should take it in turns to write and show a digital time, which their partner must then show on their model analogue clock. They should also each say a time and then find the time interval between them.

Common misconceptions
Children do not understand the way time changes when it crosses the hour. Provide frequent practice using individual clocks and whiteboards, making up given times near the hour border, and then five/ten minutes after.

Probing questions
● How long have you been at this school? What would be the most suitable units of time to record this?
● A TV programme starts at 7.50 and finishes at 8.30. How long was it on for? Explain how you worked that out.

Next steps
Support: Ask the children to work in small groups, practising making up given times on analogue clocks (initially to five-minute intervals, but extending to one-minute intervals). See also Year 3 Block D Unit 1.
Extension: Ask these children to cut out the clock faces and times on the resource sheet 'Clocks' and use them to play a pairs game where they have to match the digital times with the times shown on the analogue clock faces. See also Year 4 Block D Unit 3.

BLOCK D

Unit 2 ▦ Calculating, measuring and understanding shape

Introduction

In this unit, children solve one- and two-step word problems involving numbers, money, measures or time, using standard metric units and reading from partly numbered scales. They find areas and perimeters of rectangles, measure angles in degrees and use compass points. Children continue to develop multiplication and division, tables to 10 × 10 and multiplying by 10 or 100. They double two-digit numbers and use written methods to multiply and divide two-digit numbers by one-digit numbers, rounding remainders. They carry out addition and subtraction, using both mental and written methods. Children use a calculator for some calculations.

Framework objectives	Assessment focuses		Success criteria for Year 4	Learning outcomes
	Level 4	Level 3		
① Problem solving				
Solve one-step and two-step problems involving numbers, money or measures, including time; choose and carry out appropriate calculations, using calculator methods where appropriate	● develop own strategies for solving problems, e.g. ● make their own suggestions of ways to tackle a range of problems ● make connections to previous work ● pose and answer questions related to a problem ● check answers and ensure solutions make sense In the context of the problem ● review their work and approaches ● solve problems with or without a calculator, e.g. ● solve two-step problems choosing appropriate operations ● deal with two constraints simultaneously ● interpret a calculator display of 4.5 as £4.50 in context of money ● carry out simple calculations involving negative numbers in context ● check the reasonableness of results with reference to the context or size of numbers	● try different approaches and find ways of overcoming difficulties that arise when they are solving problems, e.g. ● check their work and make appropriate corrections, e.g. decide that two numbers less than 100 cannot give a total more than 200 and correct the addition ● begin to look for patterns in results as they work and use them to find other possible outcomes ● use mental recall of addition and subtraction facts to 20 in solving problems involving larger numbers, e.g. ● choose to calculate mentally, on paper or with apparatus ● solve one-step whole number problems appropriately ● solve two-step problems that involve addition and subtraction	● can split a problem into number sentences ● can complete calculations to solve one- and two-step problems involving measures ● can decide when it is appropriate to use a calculator	*I can work out how to solve problems with one or two steps.* *I can solve problems involving measures and time.* *I can choose what calculation to work out and I can decide whether a calculator will help me.*
② Addition and subtraction challenge				
Refine and use efficient written methods to add and subtract two-digit and three-digit whole numbers and £.p	● use efficient written methods of addition and subtraction, e.g. ● calculate 1202 + 45 + 367 or 1025 – 336	● add and subtract three-digit numbers using written methods, e.g. ● use written methods that involve bridging 10 or 100 ● add and subtract decimals in the context of money, where bridging is not required	● uses written methods to add and subtract two- and three-digit whole numbers	*I can add and subtract a two-digit and a three-digit number using an efficient written method.*

Unit 2 ⬜ Calculating, measuring and understanding shape

Framework objectives	Assessment focuses		Success criteria for Year 4	Learning outcomes
	Level 4	Level 3		
③ Multiplication facts				
Derive and recall multiplication facts up to 10 × 10, the corresponding division facts and multiples of numbers to 10 up to the tenth multiple	● quickly derive division facts that correspond to multiplication facts up to 10 × 10 ● recall multiplication facts up to 10 × 10 and quickly derive corresponding division facts	● derive associated division facts from known multiplication facts, e.g. ● given a number sentence, use understanding of operations to create related sentences ● use mental recall of the 2, 3, 4, 5 and 10 multiplication tables	● can recall multiplication facts to 10 × 10 ● can derive division facts that link to multiplication facts to 10 × 10	*I know my tables to 10 × 10.*
④ Shopping cards				
Develop and use written methods to record, support and explain multiplication and division of two-digit numbers by a one-digit number, including division with remainders (e.g. 15 × 9, 98 ÷ 6)	● use efficient written methods of short multiplication and division	● multiply and divide two-digit numbers by 2, 3, 4 or 5 as well as 10 with whole number answers and remainders, e.g. ● calculate 49 ÷ 3	● can use written methods to multiply a two-digit number by a one-digit number ● can use written methods to divide a two-digit number by a one-digit number	*I can record how to multiply and divide a two-digit number by a one-digit number.*
⑤ Rectangular perimeters and areas				
Draw rectangles and measure and calculate their perimeters; find the area of rectilinear shapes drawn on a square grid by counting squares	● find perimeters of simple shapes and find areas by counting squares, e.g. ● use the terms 'area' and 'perimeter' accurately and consistently ● find areas by counting squares and part squares ● begin to find the area of shapes that need to be divided into rectangles	● use a wider range of measures, e.g. ● begin to understand area as a measure of surface and perimeter as a measure of length ● begin to find areas of shapes by counting squares and explain answers as a number of squares even if not using standard units such as cm² or m²	● can create a rectangle and works out its area and perimeter	*I can draw a rectangle and work out its perimeter.*
⑥ Compass turns				
Know that angles are measured in degrees and that one whole turn is 360°; compare and order angles less than 180°	● interpret, with appropriate accuracy, numbers on a range of measuring instruments, e.g. ● measure and draw angles	● use a wider range of measures, e.g. ● recognise angles as a measure of turn and know that one whole turn is 360 degrees	● can puts angles in size order ● understands angles as a part of a whole turn	*I know that angles are measured in degrees.* *I know that a whole turn is 360 degrees or four right angles.*

BLOCK D

Framework objectives	Assessment focuses		Success criteria for Year 4	Learning outcomes
	Level 4	Level 3		
⑦ Treasure hunt				
Recognise horizontal and vertical lines; use the eight compass points to describe direction; describe and identify the position of a square on a grid of squares	• use the properties of 2D and 3D shapes, e.g. ● use mathematical terms such as horizontal, vertical	• describe position and movement, e.g. ● use terms to give direction along a route	• can give directions using eight compass points • can follow directions using eight compass points • can identify the position of a square on a grid • can use the terms 'horizontal' and 'vertical'	*I can use the eight compass points.* *I can give directions, follow directions and say how good someone else's directions are.*
⑧ Know your lengths!				
Use decimal notation for tenths and hundredths and partition decimals; relate the notation to money and measurement; position one-place and two-place decimals on a number line	• order decimals to three decimal places	• begin to use decimal notation in contexts such as money, e.g. ● order decimals with one dp, or two dp in context of money ● know that £3.06 equals 306p	• can use decimal notation when measuring length • knows the relationship between units of length and ways of recording them	*I can write lengths like 5 metres and 62 centimetres using decimal points.*
Choose and use standard metric units and their abbreviations when estimating, measuring and recording length, weight and capacity; know the meaning of 'kilo', 'centi' and 'milli' and, where appropriate, use decimal notation to record measurements (e.g. 1.35m or 0.6kg)	• choose and use appropriate units and instruments • interpret, with appropriate accuracy, numbers on a range of measuring instruments, e.g. ● measure a length using mm, to within 2mm	• use non-standard units and standard metric units of length, capacity and mass in a range of contexts, e.g. ● measure a length to the nearest ½cm	• can use units of length to estimate and measure • knows the relationship between metres, centimetres and millimetres	*I can estimate and measure a length using metres, centimetres or millimetres.* *I know the relationships between metres, centimetres and millimetres.*
⑨ Accurate measuring				
Interpret intervals and divisions on partially numbered scales and record readings accurately, where appropriate to the nearest tenth of a unit	• interpret, with appropriate accuracy, numbers on a range of measuring instruments	• use non-standard units and standard metric units of mass in a range of contexts, e.g. ● read simple scales, e.g. increments of 2, 5 or 10	• can measure accurately using rulers and measuring sticks	*I can use a measuring tape, metre stick or ruler to measure a length accurately.*

BLOCK D

Activity ①

Prior learning
Children can identify the calculation needed to solve a word problem. They explain and record their methods and solutions to problems and calculations.

Framework objective
Solve one-step and two-step problems involving numbers, money or measures, including time; choose and carry out appropriate calculations, using calculator methods where appropriate

Vocabulary
problem, solution, answer, method, explain, predict, reason, reasoning, calculation, add, subtract, multiply, divide

Resources
Worksheets: Problem solving (1), (2) and (3)
Classroom resources: calculators (one per child)

① Problem solving

Hand out the worksheet 'Problem solving (1)'. Ask the children to work in pairs to write number sentences to match each problem. They can then choose whether it is appropriate to use a calculator to help them solve the problem. When they have completed the activity, encourage them to compare the strategies used.

Teacher support
Less confident learners: Ask these children to work in small groups to write number sentences.
More confident learners: Let these children work individually to solve the problems on the worksheet.

Common misconception
Children do not know which operation to use when solving a word problem.
Encourage children to discuss different problems in pairs and consider strategies. With adult support, they should highlight key vocabulary and discuss reasoning.

Probing questions
● How did you know whether to add, subtract, multiply or divide? What clues did you look for in the problem?
● What are the important things to remember when you solve a word problem?

Next steps
Support: Ask the children to complete the worksheet 'Problem solving (2)'. See also Year 4 Block D Unit 1.
Extension: Ask the children to complete the worksheet 'Problem solving (3)'. See also Year 4 Block D Unit 3.

BLOCK D

Activity ②

Prior learning
Children can use £.p notation. They can use informal written methods to add and subtract two- and three-digit numbers.

Framework objective
Refine and use efficient written methods to add and subtract two-digit and three-digit whole numbers and £.p

Vocabulary
calculate, calculation, operation, answer, method, place value, partition, thousands, digit, add, subtract, sum, total, difference, plus, minus, pound (£), penny/pence (p)

Resources
Worksheets: Addition and subtraction challenge (1) and (2)
Resource sheets: Self-assessment, 1–9 digit cards (one set per pair)

② Addition and subtraction challenge

Provide each pair of children with a set of 1–9 digit cards. Ask each child in the pair to choose three digit cards. The pairs must use these six digits to create two addition sentences involving three-digit numbers, and then two subtractions. They should work out the answer to each sentence. When they have completed this, decide whether to use the self-assessment sheet for the children to record their achievements and what they need to do next.

Teacher support
Less confident learners: Ask these children to choose one three-digit number and one two-digit number for each calculation.
More confident learners: Ask these children to make the smallest total and largest total possible, with the numbers from their digit cards.

Common misconception
Children do not know addition and subtraction facts.
Provide frequent practice of addition and subtraction facts through games or daily oral and mental starters.

Probing questions
● Explain how you did these calculations. Did anyone do it a different way?
● How do you know that is the smallest/largest total you can make with those numbers?

Next steps
Support: Ask the children to complete the worksheet 'Addition and subtraction challenge (1)'. See also Year 4 Block A Unit 3.
Extension: Ask the children to complete the worksheet 'Addition and subtraction challenge (2)'. See also Year 4 Block D Unit 3.

BLOCK D

SCHOLASTIC

Activity ③

Prior learning
Children can recall multiplication and division facts for the 2-, 3-, 4-, 5-, 6-, 8-, 9- and 10-times tables.

Framework objective
Derive and recall multiplication facts up to 10 × 10, the corresponding division facts and multiples of numbers to 10 up to the tenth multiple

Vocabulary
multiply, divide, product, pattern, multiple, problem, solution, calculation, explain, relationship, multiple

Resources
Interactive activity (ITP): Multiplication facts
Worksheets: Multiplication facts (1) and (2)
Resource sheet: Self-assessment
Classroom resources: whiteboards and pens

③ Multiplication facts

Open the ITP 'Multiplication facts'. Set the rows at 7 and the columns at 8. Click on the grid and counter icon to create an array of circular counters. Ask the children how many columns and rows there are (count with them, if necessary). Ask them to write on their whiteboards two multiplications and two divisions that could describe this array. Ask: *What is 8 × 70?* By changing the rows and columns, repeat for several other arrays. Once they have completed this, decide whether to use the self-assessment sheet for the children to record their achievements and what they need to do next.

Teacher support
Less confident learners: Provide adult support and let these children work in pairs on the ITP.
More confident learners: Ask the children to work in pairs. One child should write a multiplication sentence and challenge their partner to create a matching array and derive the corresponding division.

Common misconception
Children can recite tables facts but cannot give answers out of order.
Provide frequent practice to improve speed of recall, using games and quizzes.

Probing questions
● 7 × 8 = 56. What is 56 ÷ 8?
● What could these numbers be: □ × □ = 48? How do you know? Did anyone get a different answer?

Next steps
Support: Provide the worksheet 'Multiplication facts (1)'. Ask the children to write in the factors for each number. See also Year 4 Block B Unit 3.
Extension: Provide the worksheet 'Multiplication facts (2)'. Ask the children to write in the factors for each number. How can they use these to help them create a division for each factor seed? See also Year 4 Block E Unit 1.

Activity ④

Prior learning
Children can recall multiplication and division facts for the 2-, 3-, 4-, 5-, 6-, 8-, 9- and 10-times tables. They can multiply one- and two-digit numbers by 10 and 100. They can use informal written methods to multiply and divide two-digit numbers.

Framework objective
Develop and use written methods to record, support and explain multiplication and division of two-digit numbers by a one-digit number, including division with remainders (for example, 15 × 9, 98 ÷ 6)

Vocabulary
answer, method, explain, predict, reason, reasoning, pattern, relationship, rule, place value, partition, digit, multiply, divide, product, multiple, quotient, remainder

Resources
Worksheets: Shopping cards (1), (2) and (3)
Resource sheet: Self-assessment
Classroom resources: 1-9 digit cards (one set per pair)

④ Shopping cards

Provide each pair of children with one set of cards from the worksheet 'Shopping cards (1)' and one set of 1-9 digit cards. Ask the children to place each set of cards face down and to take it in turns to take one from each set. They must then multiply the price on the shopping card by the digit card chosen (for example, 75p × 6), using an efficient written method. They should check their calculation by using the inverse operation (division). Decide whether to use the self-assessment sheet for the children to record their achievements and what they need to do next.

Teacher support
Less confident learners: Ask these children to work in small groups with adult support (or individually with a more confident learner). Supply them with blank grids for their multiplications.
More confident learners: Ask these children to work with a less confident learner and explain how to work out each calculation.

Common misconception
Children do not understand the link between division and subtraction.
Demonstrate repeated subtraction, using jumps of equal size on a number line.

Probing questions
● Pens are 82p each. How much will seven pens cost? Could you use this to help you work out the cost of 70 pens? How did you do it?
● Five boxes of wax crayons cost £2.25. How much are they each? Explain how you worked it out.

Next steps
Support: Let these children use the worksheet 'Shopping cards (2)' to play the shopping game (this worksheet shows items with lower prices). Support the group with their written methods. See also Year 4 Block A Unit 3.
Extension: Ask children to complete the worksheet 'Shopping cards (3)'. See also Year 4 Block E Unit 3.

Activity ⑤

Prior learning
Children can recall the relationships between kilometres and metres, metres and centimetres. They choose and use appropriate units to estimate, measure and record length.

Framework objective
Draw rectangles and measure and calculate their perimeters; find the area of rectilinear shapes drawn on a square grid by counting squares

Vocabulary
measure, estimate, metric unit, standard unit, length, distance, perimeter, area, kilometre (km), metre (m), centimetre (cm), millimetre, ruler, square centimetre

Resources
Display page: Perimeter and area
Resource sheet: Self-assessment
Classroom resources: squared paper

⑤ Rectangular perimeters and areas

Reveal the display page 'Perimeter and area'. Tell the children that the length of each small square represents 1cm. Ask them to work out the perimeter and area of each rectangle displayed. Decide whether to use the self-assessment sheet for the children to record their achievements and what they need to do next.

Teacher support
Less confident learners: Working in pairs, ask these children to take it in turns to draw a different-sized rectangle on squared paper. Their partner then works out the perimeter and the area.
More confident learners: Ask these children to work individually, using squared paper. Ask questions such as: *How many different rectangles can you create with a perimeter of 24cm? What are their areas?*

Common misconception
Children do not know how to find the perimeter of a shape.
Work with a small group. Mark out a rectangle 2m long and 1m wide in the playground. Ask a child to walk around the edge. Ask how we could find out how far they have walked. Share different methods of working out the perimeter and compare answers.

Probing questions
● A square has a perimeter of 32cm. How long is each side? How did you work it out?
● I need some beading for my wooden floor. The room is 6m long and 7m wide. How much beading do I need? What is the area of my wooden floor? Explain how you know.

Next steps
Support: Ask the children to work in pairs. They should measure small rectangular objects (shorter than 30cm) and then work out the perimeter and area of each shape. See also Year 3 Block B Unit 3.
Extension: Working in pairs, ask the children to take it in turns to draw, on squared paper, an irregular shape with straight sides and right angles. Their partner should then work out the area and perimeter of each shape. See also Year 5 Block D Unit 2.

BLOCK D

Activity ⑥

Prior learning

Children can use a set-square to draw right angles and to identify right angles in 2D shapes; they can compare angles with a right angle. They are able to recognise that a straight line is equivalent to two right angles.

Framework objective

Know that angles are measured in degrees and that one whole turn is 360°; compare and order angles less than 180°

Vocabulary

straight line, full turn, angle, right angle, set-square, degrees, compare, order

Resources

Worksheets: Compass turns (1), (2) and (3)
Classroom resources: set-squares, tracing paper

⑥ Compass turns

Hand out copies of the worksheet 'Compass turns (1)' and ask the children to complete it.

Teacher support

Less confident learners: Provide tracing paper for these children to use to draw in angles on the compass. This will help them when answering the questions on the worksheet.

More confident learners: Ask these children to use a ruler or a set-square to draw a selection of angles. They should then number them in order of size, and sort them into groups of 'larger than a right angle' and 'smaller than a right angle'.

Common misconception

Children think that an angle with longer arms is larger than an angle with shorter arms.

Trace one angle and lay it over other angles to compare relative sizes.

Probing questions

● Draw me an angle that is bigger than a right angle.
● Show me another right angle in this room.
● Show me two angles that are the same size. How could you prove it?

Next steps

Support: Provide these children with copies of the worksheet 'Compass turns (2)' to complete. See also Year 3 Block D Unit 3.

Extension: Ask these children to complete the worksheet 'Compass turns (3)'. See also Year 4 Block D Unit 3.

Activity ⑦

Prior learning
Children can use four compass directions to describe direction (N, S, E, W).

Framework objective
Recognise horizontal and vertical lines; use the eight compass points to describe direction; describe and identify the position of a square on a grid of squares

Vocabulary
position, direction, north-east (NE), north-west (NW), south-west (SW), south-east (SE), clockwise, anticlockwise, right angle, horizontal, vertical, grid

Resources
Worksheet: Treasure hunt
Classroom resources: squared paper

⑦ Treasure hunt

Give each child a copy of the worksheet 'Treasure hunt'. Ask them to work in pairs. They should take it in turns to choose to hide their treasure somewhere in the British Isles and identify the place as a square on the map on the worksheet. They then give their partner instructions as to how to reach the treasure from the black spot near the bottom of the grid. Encourage the children to use appropriate directional vocabulary (see list above).

Teacher support
Less confident learners: Provide these children with a list of appropriate vocabulary to use as they give instructions to their partner in the treasure hunt.
More confident learners: Encourage these children to give indirect routes to their partners.

Common misconception
Children are unable to find squares on the grid correctly.
Provide plenty of opportunities for the children to practise finding given squares in small groups.

Probing questions
● Jack is facing south. He turns through 1½ right angles. Which direction will he be facing?
● I start on the black spot and go north 4 squares, turn clockwise through 2 right angles and go forward 3 squares. Which square am I on? Did you move vertically or horizontally?

Next steps
Support: Provide squared paper. Ask each child to create a simple pattern using one colour and white. They should then give directions to their partner, to enable them to recreate the pattern. See also Year 4 Block D Unit 1.
Extension: Provide squared paper. Ask each child to create a simple pattern using two colours and white. They should then give directions to their partner, to enable them to recreate the pattern. See also Year 5 Block D Unit 1.

BLOCK D

Activity ⑧

Prior learning

Children can use £.p notation. They can read, write, partition and order whole numbers to 1000. They can recall the relationships between kilometres and metres, metres and centimetres, kilograms and grams, litres and millilitres.

Framework objectives

● Use decimal notation for tenths and hundredths and partition decimals; relate the notation to money and measurement; position one-place and two-place decimals on a number line

● **Choose and use standard metric units and their abbreviations when estimating, measuring and recording length, weight and capacity; know the meaning of 'kilo', 'centi' and 'milli' and, where appropriate, use decimal notation to record measurements (for example, 1.35m or 0.6kg)**

Vocabulary

decimal point, decimal place, tenths, hundredths, pound (£), penny/pence (p), compare, order, measure, estimate, metric unit, standard unit, length, distance, ruler, measuring tape, units of measurement and abbreviations: kilometre (km), metre (m), centimetre (cm), millimetre

Resources

Interactive activity: Know your lengths!
Worksheets: Know your lengths! (1) and (2)
Classroom resources: whiteboards and pens

⑧ Know your lengths!

Show the children the interactive activity 'Know your lengths!'. In this activity the children are required to drag labels showing different measurements to join the correct illustrations above.

Teacher support

Less confident learners: Let these children work in pairs on the interactive activity. If necessary, provide a length conversion chart for them to refer to.
More confident learners: Ask these children to estimate and measure the length of several classroom objects. Tell them to choose the most appropriate unit for each measurement. Ask: *How long would ten of each object be?*

Common misconception

Children do not know the relationships between the units of length.
Give children a length conversion chart and encourage them to learn it. They could use it to work out the equivalent of 2, 5 or 10 of a chosen unit. For example: *How many centimetres is equivalent to two metres?*

Probing questions

● What unit would you use to measure the length of the classroom? Or the length of your finger? Or the distance from here to the town centre?
● Can you think of another way to say 3m?
● Which of these is longer - 342cm or 3.24m? Why?

Next steps

Support: Ask these children to complete the worksheet 'Know your lengths! (1)'. See also Year 4 Block C Unit 2.
Extension: Provide these children with copies of the worksheet 'Know your lengths! (2)' and ask them to complete it. See also Year 5 Block C Unit 1.

Activity ⑨

Prior learning
Children can recall the relationships between kilometres and metres, metres and centimetres. They can read, to the nearest division and half division, scales that are numbered or partially numbered.

Framework objective
Interpret intervals and divisions on partially numbered scales and record readings accurately, where appropriate to the nearest tenth of a unit

Vocabulary
measure, estimate, metric unit, standard unit, length, distance, ruler, measuring tape, units of measurement and abbreviations: kilometre (km), metre (m), centimetre (cm), millimetre

Resources
Display page: Accurate measuring
Resource sheet: Self-assessment
Classroom resources: sheets of paper, pencils, 30cm rulers (marked in half centimetres on one side and millimetres on the other side)

⑨ Accurate measuring

Reveal the display page 'Accurate measuring'. Ask the children to use their rulers to draw accurately the lengths shown. They should write under each line its length in millimetres and its equivalent length in centimetres and millimetres. They should then draw an empty number line, marking on it 0 and 30, and estimate and mark on the line the position of each length. When everyone has finished, invite the children to exchange their work with a partner, who can check the lines and conversions for accuracy. Decide whether to use the self-assessment sheet for the children to record their achievements and what they need to do next.

Teacher support
Less confident learners: Let these children work in pairs. When they have finished, they can exchange their work with another pair.
More confident learners: Ask these children to draw three different lines that total 135mm in length. They can then set similar challenges for others.

Common misconception
Children do not understand that 1.3cm = 13mm when looking at a ruler.
Practise converting centimetres to millimetres and millimetres to centimetres. Compare equivalent measurements on a ruler.

Probing questions
● Explain how to measure the length of this pen accurately.
● Explain how you would measure round my head. If the measurement is between 40 and 50 centimetres, how could you record it accurately?

Next steps
Support: Ask the children to work in pairs, drawing several lines between 0cm and 30cm long for their partner to measure. See also Year 4 Block C Unit 1.
Extension: Ask the children to measure several objects that are longer than 1m. They should record the measurements in metres, and enter their measurements on an empty number line. See also Year 4 Block D Unit 3.

BLOCK D

Unit 3 ■ Calculating, measuring and understanding shape

Introduction
In this unit, children solve one-step and two-step word problems involving numbers, money, measures or time. They use standard metric units, reading from partly numbered scales. They use am, pm and the 12-hour clock to find time intervals. They find areas and perimeters of rectangles, measure angles in degrees and use compass points. They use written methods for addition and subtraction, using a calculator for some calculations.

Framework objectives	Assessment focuses		Success criteria for Year 4	Learning outcomes
	Level 4	Level 3		
① Classroom carpet				
Solve one-step and two-step problems involving numbers, money or measures, including time; choose and carry out appropriate calculations, using calculator methods where appropriate	• develop own strategies for solving problems, e.g. ● make their own suggestions of ways to tackle a range of problems ● make connections to previous work ● pose and answer questions related to a problem ● check answers and ensure solutions make sense in the context of the problem ● review their work and approaches • solve problems with or without a calculator, e.g. ● solve two-step problems choosing appropriate operations ● deal with two constraints simultaneously ● interpret a calculator display of 4.5 as £4.50 in context of money ● carry out simple calculations involving negative numbers in context • check the reasonableness of results with reference to the context or size of numbers	• try different approaches and find ways of overcoming difficulties that arise when they are solving problems, e.g. ● check their work and make appropriate corrections, e.g. decide that two numbers less than 100 cannot give a total more than 200 and correct the addition ● begin to look for patterns in results as they work and use them to find other possible outcomes • use mental recall of addition and subtraction facts to 20 in solving problems involving larger numbers, e.g. ● choose to calculate mentally, on paper or with apparatus ● solve one-step whole number problems appropriately ● solve two-step problems that involve addition and subtraction	• can solve two-step problems involving area and perimeter • uses calculator methods when appropriate to solve problems involving measures	*I can choose what calculation to work out and I can decide whether a calculator will help me.* *I can work out how to solve problems with one or two steps.* *I can solve problems involving measures and time.*
Draw rectangles and measure and calculate their perimeters; find the area of rectilinear shapes drawn on a square grid by counting squares	• find perimeters of simple shapes and find areas by counting squares, e.g. ● use the terms 'area' and 'perimeter' accurately and consistently ● find areas by counting squares and part squares ● begin to find the area of shapes that need to be divided into rectangles	• use a wider range of measures, e.g. ● begin to understand area as a measure of surface and perimeter as a measure of length ● begin to find areas of shapes by counting squares and explain answers as a number of squares even if not using standard units such as cm² or m²	• can find the area of rectilinear shapes • can find the perimeter of rectilinear shapes	*I can find the area of shapes by counting squares.*

Unit 3 📖 Calculating, measuring and understanding shape

Framework objectives	Assessment focuses		Success criteria for Year 4	Learning outcomes
	Level 4	**Level 3**		
② What's my problem?				
Refine and use efficient written methods to add and subtract two-digit and three-digit whole numbers and £.p	• use efficient written methods of addition and subtraction, e.g. ◦ calculate 1202 + 45 + 367 or 1025 − 336	• add and subtract three-digit numbers using written method, e.g. ◦ use written methods that involve bridging 10 or 100 ◦ add and subtract decimals in the context of money, where bridging is not required	• can add and subtract two- and three-digit number using a written method	*I can use written methods to add and subtract measurements made in our classroom.*
③ What's my angle?				
Know that angles are measured in degrees and that one whole turn is 360°; compare and order angles less than 180°	• interpret, with appropriate accuracy, numbers on a range of measuring instruments, e.g. ◦ measure and draw angles	• use a wider range of measures, e.g. ◦ recognise angles as a measure of turn and know that one whole turn is 360 degrees	• can compare angles by their size • can sort angles into less than 90° / more than 90° but less than 180° / right-angled	*I know if an angle is smaller than 180°. I can put a set of angles in order, from smallest to largest. I can estimate in degrees the size of an angle less than a right angle.*
④ How full are the jugs?				
Interpret intervals and divisions on partially numbered scales and record readings accurately, where appropriate to the nearest tenth of a unit	• interpret, with appropriate accuracy, numbers on a range of measuring instruments	• use non-standard units and standard metric units of capacity in a range of contexts, e.g. ◦ read simple scales, e.g. increments of 2, 5 or 10	• can read the capacity of containers using partially numbered scales	*I can read the scale on a measuring cylinder or measuring jug.*
Use decimal notation for tenths and hundredths and partition decimals; relate the notation to money and measurement; position one-place and two-place decimals on a number line	• order decimals to three decimal places	• begin to use decimal notation in contexts such as money, e.g. ◦ order decimals with one dp, or two dp in context of money ◦ know that £3.06 equals 306p	• can use decimal notation to read and record capacity measurements	*I can order decimals on a number line.*

Unit 3 📖 Calculating, measuring and understanding shape

Framework objectives	Assessment focuses		Success criteria for Year 4	Learning outcomes
	Level 4	Level 3		
⑤ How much does it hold?				
Choose and use standard metric units and their abbreviations when estimating, measuring and recording length, weight and capacity; know the meaning of 'kilo', 'centi' and 'milli' and, where appropriate, use decimal notation to record measurements (e.g. 1.35m or 0.6kg)	• choose and use appropriate units and instruments • interpret, with appropriate accuracy, numbers on a range of measuring instruments	• use non-standard units and standard metric units of capacity in a range of contexts	• can use appropriate measuring tools to measure the capacity of differently sized containers • can estimate and compare the capacity of differently sized containers	*I can estimate and measure a capacity.* *I know the relationship between litres and millilitres.* *I can write a capacity in litres using a decimal point.*
⑥ Timetables				
Read time to the nearest minute; use am, pm and 12-hour clock notation; choose units of time to measure time intervals; calculate time intervals from clocks and timetables	• use units of time, e.g. • calculate time durations that go over the hour • read and interpret timetables	• use standard units of time, e.g. • read a 12-hour clock and generally calculate time durations that do not go over the hour	• can read the time on an analogue clock to the nearest minute • can calculate time durations • can interpret timetables	*I can solve time problems where I have to work out start and finish times.* *I can use a timetable.*

BLOCK D

Activity ①

Prior learning
Children can identify the calculation needed to solve a word problem. They can explain and record their methods and solutions to problems and calculations. They can recall the relationships between kilometres and metres, metres and centimetres. They can choose and use appropriate units to estimate, measure and record length.

Framework objectives
● Solve one-step and two-step problems involving numbers, money or measures, including time; choose and carry out appropriate calculations, using calculator methods where appropriate
● Draw rectangles and measure and calculate their perimeters; find the area of rectilinear shapes drawn on a square grid by counting squares

Vocabulary
problem, solution, answer, method, explain, predict, reason, reasoning, calculation, add, subtract, multiply, divide, measure, estimate, metric unit, standard unit, length, distance, perimeter, area, kilometre (km), metre (m), centimetre (cm), millimetre, ruler, square centimetre

Resources
Worksheet: Classroom carpet
Classroom resources: calculators, squared paper

① Classroom carpet

Ask the children to work in small groups to complete the worksheet 'Classroom carpet'. They first need to decide who will do each part of the task and what roles they will play. Tell them they may use squared paper and calculators to help them solve the problem. When the children have finished, ask each group to choose a representative to explain to the rest of the class what they did to solve the problem. The representatives can then share their methods with the rest of the class. Encourage the children to compare the different methods used by each group.

Teacher support
Less confident learners: Ask these children to work in small groups with adult support. Ensure that they transfer the plan of the classroom to squared paper before trying to solve the problem.
More confident learners: Ask these children to work together to create a similar problem for other groups to solve (using only rectangles or combinations of rectangles).

Common misconception
Children have difficulty working out the perimeter or area of shapes made from combinations of rectangles.
Encourage children to divide the shape into separate rectangles before working out area or perimeter.

Probing questions
● How did knowing the length and width of the wet area help you to work out the perimeter of the rest of the classroom?
● What calculation did you use to work out the length of gripper rod needed?
● How did you work out the area of carpet needed?

Next steps
Support: Provide squared paper. In pairs, children take it in turns to create rectangles or squares and challenge their partner to find the area and perimeter. See also Year 4 Block D Unit 2.

BLOCK D

Extension: Provide these children with sheets of squared paper. Working in pairs, the children take it in turns to create shapes made from combinations of rectangles and challenge their partner to find the area and perimeter. See also Year 5 Block D Unit 1.

Activity ②

Prior learning
Children can use £.p notation. They can use informal written methods to add and subtract two- and three-digit numbers.

Framework objective
Refine and use efficient written methods to add and subtract two-digit and three-digit whole-numbers and £.p

Vocabulary
calculate, calculation, operation, answer, method, place value, partition, thousands, digit, add, subtract, sum, total, difference, plus, minus, pound (£), penny/pence (p)

Resources
Worksheet: What's my problem?
Resource sheet: Self-assessment

② What's my problem?

Say to the children: *The answer is 650ml. What is my problem?* Ask the children to create two problems, one involving addition and one involving subtraction. When they have finished this, choose different children to share their problems. Record them on the board and discuss strategies for solving them. Decide whether to use the self-assessment sheet for the children to record their achievements and what they need to do next.

Teacher support
Less confident learners: Let these children work in pairs. If necessary, give them a two-digit answer for which they need to create problems.
More confident learners: Ask these children to think up a three- or four-digit answer and challenge their partner to create problems for it.

Common misconception
Children do not correctly align hundreds, tens and units.
Encourage children to name each column before writing down any digits. They could also write each calculation on squared paper, with one column of squares for one place value.

Probing questions
● What tips would you give to help someone work this out?
● Explain why you chose to use column addition/subtraction.
● What mistake has this person made? What advice could you give them to prevent similar mistakes?

Next steps
Support: Ask the children to complete the worksheet 'What's my problem?' with adult support. See also Year 4 Block D Unit 2.
Extension: Ask the children to complete the worksheet 'What's my problem?' independently, then invite them to prepare similar problems for a partner to solve. See also Year 5 Block A Unit 1.

BLOCK D

■SCHOLASTIC

Activity ③

Prior learning
Children can use a set-square to draw right angles and to identify right angles in 2D shapes. They can compare angles with a right angle, and can recognise that a straight line is equivalent to two right angles.

Framework objective
Know that angles are measured in degrees and that one whole turn is 360°; compare and order angles less than 180°

Vocabulary
straight line, full turn, angle, right angle, set-square, degrees, compare, order, 90°, 180°, 360°

Resources
Interactive activity: What's my angle?
Worksheets: What's my angle? (1) and (2)
Classroom resources: set-squares or right-angle measurers

③ What's my angle?

Open the interactive activity 'What's my angle?'. In this activity, the children are asked to match the correct labels to a range of angles displayed on the screen. Invite them to explain their decisions.

Teacher support
Less confident learners: Provide set-squares or right-angle measurers for children to use to compare with the pictures on the screen.
More confident learners: Ask these children to use a ruler to draw their own angles to match the on-screen labels and estimate the size of the angles.

Common misconception
Children do not understand what an angle is.
Encourage children to colour in the angle before measuring or estimating.

Probing questions
- Which of these angles is biggest? How do you know?
- Which of these angles is less than 90°? Estimate its size.

Next steps
Support: Ask the children to complete the worksheet 'What's my angle? (1)'. See also Year 4 Block D Unit 2.
Extension: Provide these children with copies of the worksheet 'What's my angle? (2)' and ask them to complete it. See also Year 5 Block D Unit 2.

BLOCK D

Activity ④

Prior learning
Children can use £.p notation. They can read, write, partition and order whole numbers to 1000. They can recall the relationships between kilometres and metres, metres and centimetres, kilograms and grams, litres and millilitres. They can read, to the nearest division and half division, scales that are numbered or partially numbered.

Framework objectives
● Use decimal notation for tenths and hundredths and partition decimals; relate the notation to money and measurement; position one-place and two-place decimals on a number line
● Interpret intervals and divisions on partially numbered scales and record readings accurately, where appropriate to the nearest tenth of a unit

Vocabulary
decimal point, decimal place, tenths, hundredths, compare, order, measure, estimate, metric unit, standard unit, capacity, units of measurement and abbreviations: litre, millilitre

Resources
Interactive activities: Matching capacities, Measuring jug
Classroom resources: measuring jugs (one-litre capacity)

④ How full are the jugs?

Use the interactive activity 'Matching capacities'. Ask the children to work in pairs to match the labels to the illustrations. As they complete the activity, ask questions such as: *How did you know that label matched this jug? Which jug holds the most/least?*

Teacher support
Less confident learners: Working in pairs, ask these children to take it in turns to fill a litre jug to capacities chosen by their partner.
More confident learners: Let these children use the interactive activity 'Measuring jug' to explore filling and emptying the jug to different capacities. Encourage them to work out how much the jug would hold if, for example, another 250ml were added to it.

Common misconception
Children have difficulty reading scales.
Practise reading scales with different marked intervals (for example, in steps of 1, 2, 5, or 10).

Probing questions
● Which is smaller, 425ml or 0.5 litres? How do you know?
● Look at this jug. How much would be left in it if I poured out 325ml? Explain how you worked it out.

Next steps
Support: Let these children work in small groups with adult support. Using the interactive activity 'Measuring jug', ask them to fill the jug to varying amounts with different scales (use the tabs on the left-hand side of the screen to access jugs featuring different scales). Let the children take it in turns to read the capacity from the scale and convert to litres (for example 400 millilitres is the same as 0.4 litres). Vary the activity by giving the children an amount in litres, so they can fill the jug in millilitres. See also Year 4 Block C Unit 2.
Extension: Ask the children to set each other problems using the interactive activity 'Measuring jug'. See also Year 5 Block C Unit 2.

BLOCK D

SCHOLASTIC

Activity ⑤

Prior learning
Children can recall the relationships between kilometres and metres, metres and centimetres, kilograms and grams, litres and millilitres.

Framework objective
Choose and use standard metric units and their abbreviations when estimating, measuring and recording length, weight and capacity; know the meaning of 'kilo', 'centi' and 'milli' and, where appropriate, use decimal notation to record measurements (for example, 1.35m or 0.6kg)

Vocabulary
decimal point, decimal place, tenths, hundredths, compare, order, measure, estimate, metric unit, standard unit, capacity, units of measurement and abbreviations: litre, millilitre

Resources
Resource sheet: Self-assessment
Classroom resources: collection of different-sized containers (such as a cup, a two-litre bottle, teaspoon, large saucepan, milk jug, large mixing bowl – label each one from A to F), labels showing the volume of the chosen containers (2 litres, 5ml, 150ml and so on)

⑤ How much does it hold?

Ask the children to work in small groups, with each group choosing a leader and a scribe. Give each group a collection of containers and a set of labels. Within their groups, the children should take it in turns to choose a label and match it to a container, explaining their choice to other group members. Do other members agree? They should work together to come to an agreed result, which can be reported to the rest of the class. When they have completed the activity, decide whether to use the self-assessment sheet for the children to record their achievements and what they need to do next.

Teacher support
Less confident learners: Let these children work in mixed attainment groups, so more confident learners can support the less confident.
More confident learners: Ask these children to work in mixed attainment groups, so more confident learners can support the less confident.

Common misconception
Children do not know equivalent measurements.
Play 'snap' games, matching equivalent capacity measurements.

Probing questions
● What unit would you choose to measure the capacity of a paddling pool? Why?
● Which would you prefer, 325ml of juice or ¼ litre? How did you work it out?

Next steps
Support: Ask these children to work in groups and to measure the amounts in different containers. See also Year 4 Block C Unit 2.
Extension: Ask the children to use a two-litre container and a 750ml container to fill a five-litre container. Ask them to explain their methods. See also Year 5 Block C Unit 2.

BLOCK D

Activity ⑥

Prior learning
Children can read the time on a 12-hour digital clock and to the nearest five minutes on an analogue clock. They can calculate time intervals and find start or end times for a given time interval.

Framework objective
Read time to the nearest minute; use am, pm and 12-hour clock notation; choose units of time to measure time intervals; calculate time intervals from clocks and timetables

Vocabulary
time, am, pm, digital, analogue, timetable, arrive, depart, hour (h), minute (min), second (s)

Resources
Worksheets: Timetable (1), (2) and (3)
Classroom resources: analogue clocks

⑥ Timetables

Ask the children to complete the worksheet 'Timetable (1)'. When they have finished, say: *Maths starts at 10.35 am each morning. Show that on your clocks. School finishes at 3.20pm. Show that on your clocks.* Repeat for other subjects and times.

Teacher support
Less confident learners: Ask these children to work in pairs as they complete the worksheet.
More confident learners: Ask these children to work out the total time spent on each subject over one week and then over a six-week half term.

Common misconception
Children forget that there are 60 minutes in one hour when adding minutes together.
Practise converting a given number of minutes to hours and minutes (for example, 210 minutes is equal to 3 hours 30 minutes).

Probing questions
● How long does ICT last for? How long do we spend on ICT over a six-week half term? How did you work that out?
● Worship ends at 10.20am. How long is morning break? How long do we have for lunch and morning breaks each week?

Next steps
Support: Provide these children with the worksheet 'Timetable (2)' and ask them to complete it. See also Year 4 Block D Unit 1.
Extension: Ask these children to complete the worksheet 'Timetable (3)'. See also Year 5 Block D Unit 1.

BLOCK D

Periodic assessment

These activities can be used at any time during the teaching of this block to assess those children that you think have achieved the objective. A grid highlighting the related assessment focuses and expected learning outcomes for each activity can be found on the CD-ROM.

Multiplication and division

Framework objectives
● Derive and recall multiplication facts up to 10 × 10, the corresponding division facts and multiples of numbers to 10 up to the tenth multiple
● Develop and use written methods to record, support and explain multiplication and division of two-digit numbers by a one-digit number

Learning outcomes
● I know my tables to 10 × 10.
● I can record how to multiply and divide a two-digit number by a one-digit number.

Part 1
To assess children's knowledge of multiplication and division facts to 10 × 10, use the worksheet 'Multiplication and division'. This is a quick-fire mental test, to be delivered orally, allowing about 5 seconds per question. It should be marked together so that children can see which facts they know.

Part 2
To assess children using written methods for multiplication and division, write on the board: 27 × 8, 68 × 9, 78 ÷ 3, 85 ÷ 4. Ask the children to choose a suitable written method to work out the answers for each calculation. Mark the answers and methods together, so children can see what they can do. Choose different children to explain their method. Discuss and compare strategies for overcoming difficulties.

Measuring

Framework objective
Choose and use standard metric units and their abbreviations when estimating, measuring and recording length, weight and capacity; know the meaning of 'kilo', 'centi' and 'milli' and, where appropriate, use decimal notation to record measurements (for example, 1.3m or 0.6kg)

Learning outcomes
● I can estimate and measure a weight. I know the relationships between units of weight. I can write a mass in kilograms using a decimal point.
● I can estimate and measure a length using m, cm or mm. I know the relationships between metres, centimetres and millimetres.
● I can estimate and measure a capacity. I know the relationship between litres and millilitres. I can write a capacity in litres using a decimal point.

Mass
Use three equal-sized boxes, with 50g, 500g and 1kg weights inside. Ask the children to estimate and then weigh each box. *Which was heaviest/lightest?* Order the boxes from lightest to heaviest. Record the weights in g and kg.

Length
Use a ruler, a metre rule and a tape measure. Ask children to estimate, and then measure the following: (a) length of a book; (b) circumference of a football; (c) height of a door. Record each measurement in centimetres and metres. Order the lengths.

Capacity
Use a yoghurt pot, a large bowl and a litre jug marked in 100ml intervals. Ask the children to estimate and record the capacity of each container, in millilitres and litres. *How many yoghurt pots would fill the bowl? Test your estimates using the measuring jug.*

When the children have completed the activities, decide whether to use the self-assessment sheet for them to record their achievements and next steps.

BLOCK D

Know your angles

Framework objective
Know that angles are measured in degrees and that one whole turn is 360°; compare and order angles less than 180°

Learning outcomes
- I know that angles are measured in degrees.
- I know that a whole turn is 360 degrees or four right angles.
- I know if an angle is smaller than 180°.
- I can put a set of angles in order, from smallest to largest.
- I can estimate in degrees the size of an angle less than a right angle.

Provide each child with a copy of the worksheet 'Know your angles' and ask them to complete it. The children will need a pencil, ruler, a 45° set-square and a 60° set-square. When they have completed the activity, ask them to identify the biggest/smallest angles. Ask: *How many degrees are there in a straight line / a full turn / a right angle?* Choose a child to explain how they used a set-square to draw an angle to a given size. What tips could they give to help someone use a set-square accurately?

BLOCK D

▨ SCHOLASTIC

Name   Date

Multiplication and division

Mental questions: Allow five seconds per question.

1. $6 \times 7 =$ .... ☐

2. $5 \times 8 =$ .... ☐

3. $9 \times 3 =$ .... ☐

4. $40 \times 7 =$ .... ☐

5. $50 \times 6 =$ .... ☐

6. $2 \times 90 =$ .... ☐

7. I save 80p per week. How much money will I have after 9 weeks?

_____

8. Stickers cost 90p a packet. How much will 6 packets cost?

_____

9. Chocolate bars are in packets of 6. How many packets do I need to buy for 40 children?

_____

10. My plant has grown 8 centimetres each week. It is now 32 centimetres tall. How old is it?

_____

11. $56 \div 7 =$ .... ☐

12. $64 \div 8 =$ .... ☐

BLOCK D

Name	Date

(continued)

13. 81 ÷ 9 = ... ☐

14. 420 ÷ 7 = ... ☐

15. 360 ÷ 60 = ... ☐

16. 240 ÷ 8 = ... ☐

17. I have just bought 4 bus tickets for £2.80. How much was each ticket?

_____

18. A box of 8 bags of potatoes weighs 40 kilograms. How much does each bag weigh?

_____

19. The total length of 6 tables is 4.8 metres. How long is each table?

_____

20. A jug holds 3.2 litres of juice. How many 40 ml cups can I fill?

_____

How easy?

Red
Amber
Green

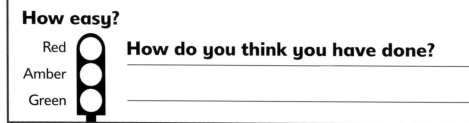

How do you think you have done?

_____

_____

BLOCK E
Securing number facts, relationships and counting

Expected prior learning
Check that children can already:
- recall multiplication facts and derive related division facts for the 2-, 3-, 4-, 5- and 10-times tables
- read and write proper fractions, e.g. $3/7$, $9/10$
- understand the terms 'denominator' (the parts of a whole) and 'numerator' (the number of parts)
- find unit fractions of numbers and quantities, e.g. $1/2$, $1/3$, $1/4$ and $1/6$ of 12 litres
- find unit fractions of shapes
- use diagrams to compare the size of two unit fractions.

Objectives overview
The text in this diagram identifies the focus of mathematics learning within the block.

Key aspects of learning
- Problem solving
- Communication
- Reasoning

Solving one- and two-step word problems involving numbers, money or measures

Representing a problem

Interpreting the solution

Tables to 10 × 10; multiples

Written methods; TU × U, TU/U; rounding remainders

BLOCK E:
Securing number facts, relationships and counting

Equivalence of fractions

Mixed numbers

Fractions of shapes and quantities

Interpreting the language of ratio and proportion

Using a calculator

BLOCK E

Unit 1 ▢ Securing number facts, relationships and counting

Introduction

In this unit, children develop their skills in solving problems and puzzles, and learn how to represent these using number statements or diagrams; this should be borne in mind for the work throughout the unit. Children work in pairs for many activities, and should be encouraged to develop their ability to respond to differing viewpoints in a pleasant and courteous manner, putting across their own point of view. They continue to develop their skills in deriving and recalling multiplication and division facts. For the final part of this unit the work is concentrated on developing understanding about fractions and decimal fractions, as well as responding to word problems and writing their own problems involving fractions and decimal fractions.

Framework objectives	Assessment focuses		Success criteria for Year 4	Learning outcomes
	Level 4	Level 3		
① How many school dinners this week?				
Represent a puzzle or problem using number sentences, statements or diagrams; use these to solve the problem; present and interpret the solution in the context of the problem	• present information and results in a clear and organised way, e.g. ● organise written work, e.g. record results in order ● begin to work in an organised way from the start ● consider appropriate units ● use related vocabulary accurately	• begin to organise their work and check results, e.g. ● begin to develop own ways of recording ● develop an organised approach as they get into recording their work on a problem • discuss their mathematical work and begin to explain their thinking, e.g. ● use appropriate mathematical vocabulary ● talk about their findings by referring to their written work • use and interpret mathematical symbols and diagrams	• can use number sentences and statements such as: ● 250 − 20 = 230 so there are 230 children in school on Monday ● 230 − 100 = 130 so 130 have school dinners on Monday • can check the answers make sense by re-reading the questions • can present and interpret the solutions in the context of the problem	I can write down number sentences or drawings to help me solve a problem. When I have solved a problem I re-read the question to make sure the answer makes sense.
② Quick recall				
Derive and recall multiplication facts up to 10 × 10, the corresponding division facts and multiples of numbers to 10 up to the tenth multiple	• quickly derive division facts that correspond to multiplication facts up to 10 × 10 • recall multiplication facts up to 10 × 10 and quickly derive corresponding division facts	• derive associated division facts from known multiplication facts, e.g. ● given a number sentence, use understanding of operations to create related sentences • use mental recall of the 2, 3, 4, 5 and 10 multiplication tables	• can recall multiplication facts, the corresponding division facts and multiples	I can tell you answers to the 2-, 3-, 4-, 5-, 6- and 10-times tables, even when they are not in the right order. If you give me a multiplication fact I can give you one or two division facts to go with it.

BLOCK E

Unit 1 📖 Securing number facts, relationships and counting

Framework objectives	Assessment focuses		Success criteria for Year 4	Learning outcomes
	Level 4	Level 3		
③ Fractions that total one whole				
Identify pairs of fractions that total 1	• recognise approximate proportions of a whole and use simple fractions and percentages to describe these	• use simple fractions that are several parts of a whole, e.g. • recognise and record fractions that are several parts of the whole such as $3/4$, $2/5$	• can use diagrams to identify pairs of fractions that add up to a whole	*Using diagrams, I can find pairs of fractions that make one whole.*
④ Match equivalent fractions				
Use diagrams to identify equivalent fractions (e.g. $6/8$ and $3/4$, or $70/100$ and $7/10$); interpret mixed numbers and position them on a number line (e.g. $3^1/_2$)	• recognise approximate proportions of a whole and use simple fractions and percentages to describe these, e.g. • recognise simple equivalence between fractions	• use simple fractions that are several parts of a whole and recognise when two simple fractions are equivalent, e.g. • recognise and record fractions that are several parts of the whole such as $3/4$, $2/5$ • recognise some fractions that are equivalent to $1/2$	• can match equivalent fractions in diagrams • recognises equivalence between written fractions	*I can use a fraction to describe a part of a whole.* *I can show you on a diagram of a rectangle made from eight squares that one half is the same as two quarters or four eighths.*
⑤ Equivalent decimals and fractions				
Recognise the equivalence between decimal and fraction forms of one half, quarters, tenths and hundredths	• recognise approximate proportions of a whole and use simple fractions and percentages to describe these, e.g. • recognise simple equivalence between fractions and decimals, e.g. $1/2$, $1/4$, $1/10$, $3/4$ • solve problems with or without a calculator, e.g. • interpret a calculator display of 4.5 as £4.50 in context of money	• begin to use decimal notation in contexts such as money, e.g. • order decimals with one dp, or two dp in context of money • know that £3.06 equals 306p	• looks at decimal fractions and can identify the equivalent fraction, including in the context of money and measures	*I know that two quarters, five tenths and fifty hundredths are the same as one half.*
⑥ Find the fraction				
Find fractions of numbers, quantities or shapes (e.g. $1/5$ of 30 plums, $3/8$ of a 6 by 4 rectangle)	• recognise approximate proportions of a whole and use simple fractions and percentages to describe these	• use simple fractions that are several parts of a whole and recognise when two simple fractions are equivalent, e.g. • understand and use unit fractions such as $1/2$, $1/4$, $1/3$, $1/5$, $1/10$ and find those fractions of shapes and sets of objects • recognise and record fractions	• can find fractions of quantities	*I can find a fraction of a shape drawn on squared paper.* *I can find a fraction of a number of cubes by sharing them in equal groups.*

BLOCK E

Activity ①

Prior learning
Children can solve simple word problems using number sentences. They present a solution in the context of a problem.

Framework objective
Represent a puzzle or problem using number sentences, statements or diagrams; use these to solve the problem; present and interpret the solution in the context of the problem

Vocabulary
problem, solution, calculator, calculate, calculation, equation, operation, symbol, inverse, answer, method, explain, predict, reason, reasoning, pattern, relationship

Resources
Worksheets: How many school dinners this week? (1), (2) and (3)

① How many school dinners this week?

Give each child a copy of the worksheet 'How many school dinners this week? (1)'. Ask the children to work individually until they have come up with a solution using pencil and paper methods. They should then present their work to a partner and compare their methods of working and finding solutions.

Teacher support
Less confident learners: Provide these children with the worksheet 'How many school dinners this week? (2)' and ask them to complete it.
More confident learners: Ask these children to complete the worksheet 'How many school dinners this week? (3)'.

Common misconception
Children have difficulty interpreting word problems.
Remind children to make pencil and paper jottings as they read the problem. At each stage, they should interpret the written statement as a number problem and find the solution.

Probing questions
● Which number operation will you use to calculate the number of children that are at school each day?
● How do you find half of a number?
● How do you find the total number of school dinners for the week?

Next steps
Support: Ask the children to work through the worksheet 'How many school dinners this week? (2)' with an adult. Then they can try the worksheet 'How many school dinners this week? (1)'. See also Year 4 Blocks A and B for examples of word problems.
Extension: Encourage the children to devise a similar problem based on another week of dinners for that school. They can give it to their partner to solve. See also Year 4 Block E Unit 2.

BLOCK E

Activity ②

Prior learning
Children can recall multiplication facts and derive related division facts for the 2-, 3-, 4-, 5- and 10-times tables.

Framework objective
Derive and recall multiplication facts up to 10 × 10, the corresponding division facts and multiples of numbers to 10 up to the tenth multiple

Vocabulary
multiply, multiplied by, divide, divided by, inverse operation

Resources
Interactive activity: Quick recall
Worksheets: Quick recall (1), (2) and (3)

② Quick recall

Ask the children to work in pairs, with one child completing the worksheet 'Quick recall (1)' while the other simultaneously completes the activity on screen 1 of the interactive activity 'Quick recall'. Who can recall the answers more quickly? Then ask the pairs to swap over and repeat the activity.

Teacher support
Less confident learners: Encourage the children to rehearse some multiplication and division facts orally first. Get them to work in pairs, sharing a multiplication square and posing quick-fire questions to each other. Once they have done this, ask them to complete the worksheet 'Quick recall (2)' and screen 2 of the interactive activity.
More confident learners: Working in pairs, ask these children to discuss how multiples of 10 can be multiplied and divided by 2, 3, 4, 5, 6, and 10. Then ask them to complete the worksheet 'Quick recall (3)'.

Common misconception
Children do not know how to use an inverse operation to help them complete an equation with the initial number missing (for example, ▢ × 2 = 8).
Practise as many examples as possible, and ask children to pose their own examples for a partner.

Probing questions
● How does knowing the answer to 8 × 3 help you to work out the answer to 80 × 3?
● How does knowing the answer to 8 × 3 help you to work out the answer to 240 ÷ 3?

Next steps
Support: Provide these children with opportunities to practise recognising and using inverse operations. See also Year 4 Blocks A, B and D.
Extension: Encourage the children to complete longer lists of quick-fire questions or to devise a list for their partner to answer. See also Year 4 Block E Units 2 and 3.

BLOCK E

Activity ③

Prior learning
Children can read and write proper fractions (for example, $3/7$, $9/10$). They understand the terms 'denominator' (the parts of a whole) and 'numerator' (the number of parts).

Framework objective
Identify pairs of fractions that total 1

Vocabulary
fraction, unit fraction, mixed number, numerator, denominator, equivalent

Resources
Interactive activity: Fractions that total one whole
Classroom resources: card

③ Fractions that total one whole

Ask the children to complete the interactive activity 'Fractions that total one whole'. In this activity they are asked to match fraction statements to diagrams on the screen.

Teacher support
Less confident learners: Check that these children understand which part of a fraction represents the number of parts (numerator) and which part represents how many parts the whole is divided into (denominator); ensure that they understand that in a whole number the numerator and denominator will be the same. Encourage them to practise writing equivalents of 1.
More confident learners: Ask these children to write two fractions equivalent to one on separate pieces of card. Repeat four times. They can then play a pairs game with a partner to reinforce the learning.

Common misconception
Children are confused as to what is meant by 'one whole'.
Give lots of examples in either visual or oral form of whole items that can be cut up or shared (for example, cakes, tube of sweets): *I have ten sweets and I eat a fifth of them. How many are left for you? Write what each fraction looks like.* ($1/5$ and $4/5$)

Probing questions
● I eat one third of a pizza and you eat the rest. What fraction of the pizza do you eat?
● Three-quarters of a class are girls. What fraction of the class are boys?
● Two-fifths of a class have school dinners. The rest have packed lunch. What fraction have packed lunch?

Next steps
Support: Provide the children with more practice on fractions as described in 'Common misconceptions' and 'Probing questions'. See also Year 3 Block E Unit 1.
Extension: Ask the children to make up fraction stories as in the examples in 'probing questions'. They could work in pairs and answer each other's questions. See also Year 4 Block E Unit 2.

Activity ④

Prior learning
Children can read and write proper fractions. They understand the terms 'denominator' (the parts of a whole) and 'numerator' (the number of parts). They can find unit fractions of numbers and quantities. They can find unit fractions of shapes. They use diagrams to compare the size of two unit fractions.

Framework objective
Use diagrams to identify equivalent fractions (for example, $^6/_8$ and $^3/_4$, or $^{70}/_{100}$ and $^7/_{10}$); interpret mixed numbers and position them on a number line (for example, $3^1/_2$)

Vocabulary
fraction, unit fraction, mixed number, numerator, denominator, equivalent

Resources
Worksheet: Match equivalent fractions
Classroom resources: squared paper

④ Match equivalent fractions

Ask the children to complete the worksheet 'Match equivalent fractions'.

Teacher support
Less confident learners: Ask these children to work in a small group with an adult to facilitate discussion.
More confident learners: When the children have completed the worksheet, give them squared paper and ask them to draw equivalents of their own, dividing whole rectangles into a larger number of parts. For example, they could show twentieths, hundredths, eighteenths and so on. Ask questions such as: *How many 20ths = $^1/_2$?*

Common misconception
Children are unsure how to interpret a shaded shape as a numerical fraction.
Remind children how to find the denominator (how many parts altogether) and how to find the numerator (how many parts are shaded).

Probing questions
● How many eighths are equal to one half?
● What is one half in tenths?
● How can you use your knowledge of times tables to work out whether two fractions are equivalent?

Next steps
Support: Use practical examples – for example, draw and cut out 'cakes' and 'pizzas' and divide them between two, three or four children. Ask: *What fraction do you each have?* Cut 'cakes' into four, six or eight parts and give each child two each so that they have $^2/_4$ instead of $^1/_2$, and so on. See also Year 3 Block E Unit 1 for more work on fractions.
Extension: Ask the children to write equivalence chain problems for a partner to solve (for example $^1/_2 = 3/\square = 8/\square = \square/30$). See also Year 4 Block E Units 2 and 3.

BLOCK E

Activity ⑤

Prior learning
Children can understand the terms 'denominator' (the parts of a whole) and 'numerator' (the number of parts).

Framework objective
Recognise the equivalence between decimal and fraction forms of one half, quarters, tenths and hundredths

Vocabulary
decimal, fraction, unit fraction, numerator, denominator, equivalent

Resources
Worksheet: Equivalent decimals and fractions

⑤ Equivalent decimals and fractions

Hand out copies of the worksheet 'Equivalent decimals and fractions' and ask the children to complete it.

Teacher support
Less confident learners: Ask these children to make, with support, a table of fraction and decimal equivalents before they start working on the worksheet 'Equivalent decimals and fractions'.
More confident learners: Challenge these children to devise their own equivalents questions for a partner to solve.

Common misconception
Children do not understand why 0.5 is the equivalent of $^1/_2$ or why 0.25 is the equivalent of $^1/_4$.
Remind children that a decimal is expressed in tenths or hundredths and that $0.5 = ^5/_{10}$, $0.25 = ^{25}/_{100}$, $^5/_{10}$ is the equivalent of $^1/_2$ and $^{25}/_{100}$ the equivalent of $^1/_4$.

Probing questions
● Explain to your partner how to remember that $0.5 = ^1/_2$ and that $0.25 = ^1/_4$ and $0.75 = ^3/_4$.

Next steps
Support: Ask these children to work in a group with an adult and use decimal examples in the context of money. Establish that 50p is half of £1 and is written as £0.50 (£0.5), 25p = a quarter of £1, and so on. See also Year 5 Block E Unit 1.
Extension: Encourage these children to write other equivalents that they know or can work out, some in the context of money and measures. See also Year 4 Block E Units 2 and 3.

Activity ⑥

<table>
<tr><td>

Prior learning
Children can find unit fractions of numbers and quantities, e.g. $^1/_2$, $^1/_3$, $^1/_4$ and $^1/_6$ of 12 litres.

</td><td>

Framework objective
Find fractions of numbers, quantities or shapes (for example, $^1/_5$ of 30 plums, $^3/_8$ of a 6 by 4 rectangle)

Vocabulary
fraction, unit fraction, mixed number, numerator, denominator, equivalent

Resources
Interactive activity: Find the fraction
Classroom resources: small counting items (counters, cubes etc)

</td></tr>
</table>

⑥ Find the fraction

Show the children the interactive activity 'Find the fraction'. In this activity they are asked to read a range of fraction questions and then select the correct answer from the options provided.

Teacher support
Less confident learners: Ask these children to work as a group and discuss the questions with a partner and/or adult supporter.
More confident learners: Ask these children to explain how they worked out the answers to the questions. You could also challenge them to write similar questions to present to the group or class.

Common misconception
Children are insecure in finding fractions of the numbers involved in the quantities.
Children may experience difficulties if they do not understand the relevance of knowing their times tables and corresponding division facts. Ask more confident learners to work with a less confident partner to develop these skills.

Probing questions
● How do you find one-fifth of a number such as 25?
● How would you then find two-fifths, three-fifths and four-fifths of this number?

Next steps
Support: Provide small objects such as counters and interlocking cubes, and ask the children to find unit fractions of different numbers of them. See also Year 3 Block E Unit 1 for practice in finding unit fractions of numbers and quantities.
Extension: Challenge the children to find one quarter, one third and one half of 8, 16, 24, 32 and 40. Ask: *What do you notice about these numbers?* See also Year 4 Block E Units 2 and 3.

BLOCK E

Unit 2 Securing number facts, relationships and counting

Introduction

In this unit, children develop their skills in solving one- and two-step word problems involving numbers, money and measures. They represent problems and interpret solutions, using a calculator when appropriate. They continue to develop their tables to 10 × 10, investigating multiples. Finally, children investigate the equivalence of fractions, mixed numbers, fractions of shapes and quantities.

Framework objectives	Assessment focuses		Success criteria for Year 4	Learning outcomes
	Level 4	Level 3		
(1) Different ways to solve problems				
Represent a puzzle or problem using number sentences, statements or diagrams; use these to solve the problem; present and interpret the solution in the context of the problem	● present information and results in a clear and organised way, e.g. ● organise written work, e.g. record results in order ● begin to work in an organised way from the start ● consider appropriate units ● use related vocabulary accurately	● begin to organise their work and check results, e.g. ● begin to develop own ways of recording ● develop an organised approach as they get into recording their work on a problem ● discuss their mathematical work and begin to explain their thinking, e.g. ● use appropriate mathematical vocabulary ● talk about their findings by referring to their written work ● use and interpret mathematical symbols and diagrams	● can use number sentences and statements, e.g. 20 metres × 30 lengths = 600m, so I swam 600m ● re-reads questions to check answers make sense	*I can write down number sentences or drawings to help me solve a problem.* *When I have solved a problem I re-read the question to make sure the answer makes sense.*
(2) The 7-times table				
Derive and recall multiplication facts up to 10 × 10, the corresponding division facts and multiples of numbers to 10 up to the tenth multiple	● quickly derive division facts that correspond to multiplication facts up to 10 × 10 ● recall multiplication facts up to 10 × 10 and quickly derive corresponding division facts	● derive associated division facts from known multiplication facts, e.g. ● given a number sentence, use understanding of operations to create related sentences ● use mental recall of the 2, 3, 4, 5 and 10 multiplication tables	● can use knowledge of the 7-times table to answer multiplication and division questions ● can find remainders when doing division	*I can tell you answers to the 7-times table, even when they are not in the right order.* *If you give me a multiplication fact I can give you one or two division facts to go with it.*

BLOCK E

148

■SCHOLASTIC

Unit 2 📖 Securing number facts, relationships and counting

Framework objectives	Assessment focuses		Success criteria for Year 4	Learning outcomes
	Level 4	**Level 3**		
③ Equivalents				
Recognise the equivalence between decimal and fraction forms of one half, quarters, tenths and hundredths	● recognise approximate proportions of a whole and use simple fractions and percentages to describe these, e.g. ● recognise simple equivalence between fractions and decimals, e.g. $1/2$, $1/4$, $1/10$, $3/4$ ● solve problems with or without a calculator, e.g. ● interpret a calculator display of 4.5 as £4.50 in context of money	● begin to use decimal notation in contexts such as money, e.g. ● order decimals with one dp, or two dp in context of money ● know that £3.06 equals 306p	● can match decimal and fraction equivalents of numbers and measures	*I can recognise decimals and fractions that are equivalent.*
④ Equivalent fractions				
Use diagrams to identify equivalent fractions (e.g. $6/8$ and $3/4$, or $70/100$ and $7/10$); interpret mixed numbers and position them on a number line (e.g. $3\tfrac{1}{2}$)	● recognise approximate proportions of a whole and use simple fractions and percentages to describe these, e.g. ● recognise simple equivalence between fractions	● use simple fractions that are several parts of a whole and recognise when two simple fractions are equivalent, e.g. ● recognise and record fractions that are several parts of the whole such as $3/4$, $2/5$ ● recognise some fractions that are equivalent to $1/2$	● can use cubes to make and explain equivalent fractions ● can use a 100-square to make and explain equivalent fractions	*I can find fractions that are equivalent to $1/4$. I can order mixed numbers and put them on a number line.*
⑤ Fractions that make one whole				
Identify pairs of fractions that total 1	● recognise approximate proportions of a whole and use simple fractions and percentages to describe these	● use simple fractions that are several parts of a whole, e.g. ● recognise and record fractions that are several parts of the whole such as $3/4$, $2/5$	● can identify two fractions that add up to make a whole one	*Using diagrams, I can find pairs of fractions that make one whole.*
⑥ Fractions of quantities				
Find fractions of numbers, quantities or shapes (e.g. $1/5$ of 30 plums, $3/8$ of a 6 by 4 rectangle)	● recognise approximate proportions of a whole and use simple fractions and percentages to describe these	● use simple fractions that are several parts of a whole and recognise when two simple fractions are equivalent, e.g. ● understand and use unit fractions such as $1/2$, $1/4$, $1/3$, $1/5$, $1/10$ and find those fractions of shapes and sets of objects ● recognise and record fractions	● can use division and multiplication to find given fractions of numbers and quantities	*I can find one fifth of a number by dividing it by 5.*

BLOCK E

Activity ①

Prior learning
Children can recall
multiplication facts
and derive related
division facts
for the 2-, 3-, 4-,
5- and 10-times
tables. They can
find unit fractions
of numbers and
quantities, such as
$\frac{1}{2}$, $\frac{1}{3}$, $\frac{1}{4}$ and $\frac{1}{6}$ of
12 litres.

Framework objective
Represent a puzzle or problem using number sentences, statements or
diagrams; use these to solve the problem; present and interpret the solution
in the context of the problem

Vocabulary
problem, solution, calculator, calculate, calculation, equation, operation,
symbol, inverse, answer, method, explain, add, subtract, multiply, multiplied
by, divide, divided by, sum, total, difference, plus, minus

Resources
Display page: Different ways to solve problems
Worksheets: Different ways to solve problems (1), (2) and (3)
Classroom resources: calculators

① Different ways to solve problems

Reveal the display page 'Different ways to solve problems' and talk through
the different questions with the children. Then hand out copies of the
corresponding worksheet 'Different ways to solve problems (1)'. Ask the
children to complete the questions using a range of different ways of doing
their jottings. Remind them that the purpose of doing this is not just to find the
answer but also to show that they can represent the problem to help someone
else understand what to do.

Teacher support
Less confident learners: Ask these children to complete the worksheet
'Different ways to solve problems (2)'.
More confident learners: Ask these children to complete the worksheet
'Different ways to solve problems (3)'.

Common misconception
Children do not refer back to earlier questions for necessary information.
Ensure that children write down or underline important facts (for example, the
length of the pool) in their jottings as they read questions.

Probing questions
● What number sentence do you need to write to solve this part of the
problem?
● When must I use multiplication to find an answer?
● How do I find a fraction of a number or length of time?

Next steps
Support: Ask the children to work in a group with an adult and write their own
examples of a problem for another group to solve. See also Year 4 Block E
Unit 1.
Extension: Invite these children to solve the problems that others have written,
and compare methods used by different groups. They could check answers with
a calculator. See also Year 4 Block E Unit 3.

Activity ②

Prior learning
Children can recall multiplication facts and derive related division facts for the 2-, 3-, 4-, 5- and 10-times tables.

Framework objective
Derive and recall multiplication facts up to 10 × 10, the corresponding division facts and multiples of numbers to 10 up to the tenth multiple

Vocabulary
multiply, multiplied by, divide, divided by, remainder, multiple, divisor

Resources
Worksheets: The 7-times table (1), (2) and (3)
Classroom resources: calculators

② The 7-times table

Ask the children to complete the worksheet 'The 7-times table (1)'.

Teacher support
Less confident learners: Ask these children to complete the worksheet 'The 7-times table (2)' first. Once they have done this, they could move on to the worksheet 'The 7-times table (1)'.
More confident learners: Extend the activity by asking these children to complete the worksheet 'The 7-times table (3)'.

Common misconception
Children have difficulty remembering some facts in the 7-times table.
Give children strategies for working out 7-times table facts (for example, using corresponding facts from the 5- and 2-times tables and adding up the two answers).

Probing questions
● How can you work out 7 × 7 if you do not know your 7-times table?
● What is a good strategy for working out remainders when you are dividing?

Next steps
Support: Practise chanting tables with children and play 'pairs' games with question and answer cards (children can prepare the cards themselves as extra practice). See also Year 4 Block E Unit 1.
Extension: Challenge these children to work in pairs to think of word problems that involve the 7-times table. They could check their answers with a calculator and then present them to other pairs to solve. See also Year 4 Block E Unit 3.

BLOCK E

Activity ③

Prior learning	**Framework objective**

Prior learning
Children can read and write proper fractions (for example, $^3/_7$, $^9/_{10}$).

Framework objective
Recognise the equivalence between decimal and fraction forms of one half, quarters, tenths and hundredths

Vocabulary
fraction, decimal fraction, mixed number, numerator, denominator, equivalent

Resources
Worksheets: Equivalents (1) and (2)
Classroom resources: calculators

③ Equivalents

Ask the children to complete the worksheet 'Equivalents (1)'.

Teacher support
Less confident learners: Ask these children to work in small groups with adult support.
More confident learners: Ask these children to write tenths, hundredths, quarters and halves as they would appear on a calculator display, using the worksheet 'Equivalents (2)'.

Common misconception
Children confuse decimal equivalents of $^1/_2$, $^1/_4$ and $^3/_4$.
Use these fractions in the context of money: £1.00 = 100p, £$^1/_2$ = 50p or £0.5, £$^1/_4$ = £0.25 or 25p and £$^3/_4$ = £0.75 or 75p. Provide different opportunities for children to practise using these facts (for example, shopping games, measuring activities and 'snap' games).

Probing questions
● What fractions are equivalent to: 0.25, 0.75, 0.1, 0.01, 0.5?

Next steps
Support: Encourage these children to practise finding fraction and decimal equivalents using a calculator. For example, 1 ÷ 2 ($^1/_2$) on a calculator = 0.5. See also Year 4 Block E Unit 1.
Extension: Extend the idea of interpreting fractions on a calculator display by challenging the children to write their own fraction problems and use a calculator to find answers. See also Year 4 Block E Unit 3.

BLOCK E

SCHOLASTIC

Activity ④

Prior learning
Children can recall multiplication facts and derive related division facts for the 2-, 3-, 4-, 5- and 10-times tables. They can read and write proper fractions. They understand the terms 'denominator' (the parts of a whole) and 'numerator' (the number of parts).

Framework objective
Use diagrams to identify equivalent fractions (for example, $^6/_8$ and $^3/_4$, or $^{70}/_{100}$ and $^7/_{10}$); interpret mixed numbers and position them on a number line (for example, $3^1/_2$)

Vocabulary
fraction, unit fraction, mixed number, numerator, denominator, equivalent

Resources
Resource sheets: Self-assessment, Blank 100-square, Multiplication square
Classroom resources: coloured paper, glue, interlocking cubes (32 for each pair of children), scissors, squared paper, blank number lines, whiteboards and pens

④ Equivalent fractions

Give each pair of children 32 interlocking cubes. Ask them to share them equally and to write down on their whiteboards what fraction they each have ($^1/_2$ or $^{16}/_{32}$). *Tell your partner about the relationship between the numerator and the denominator in these fractions: $^1/_2$, $^4/_8$, $^8/_{16}$, $^{16}/_{32}$.* Ask the children to identify a range of equivalent fractions (tenths and hundredths) on a blank 100-square. *Show and explain to your partner why $^1/_{10} = {}^{10}/_{100}$, $^2/_{10} = {}^{20}/_{100}$, $^7/_{10} = {}^{70}/_{100}$.* Ask the children to work with squared paper and cubes to show others a range of equivalent fractions. Decide whether to use the self-assessment sheet for the children to record their achievements and what they need to do next.

Teacher support
Less confident learners: Ask these children to work with an adult or a more confident learner. If necessary, they could carry out the activities involving the cubes or the 100-square only.
More confident learners: Get the children to demonstrate their understanding of mixed numbers by using, for example, three complete 100-squares and half of a 100-square. They could glue them onto coloured paper and explain to others what they have written beside them (for example, $3\frac{1}{2}$ or $3^{50}/_{100}$).

Common misconception
Children have difficulty finding equivalent fractions.
Remind children that they multiply or divide the numerator and the denominator by the same number to find an equivalent fraction. Show them how practical work with cubes generates the same answer as this strategy.

Probing questions
● How many equivalents of $^1/_2$ can you think of?
● How many equivalents of $^1/_4$ can you show with your cubes? ($^2/_8$, $^4/_{16}$, $^3/_{12}$, $^6/_{24}$)
Show me some equivalents of $^3/_4$.
● Show me $^1/_{10}$ on your 100-square. How many 100ths make one whole?

Next steps
Support: If necessary, provide a multiplication square to help these children work out equivalents. See also Year 4 Block E Unit 1.
Extension: Give these children a blank number line and ask them to create a number line from 0–5 that includes quarters, halves and three quarters. See also Year 4 Block E Unit 3.

BLOCK E

Activity ⑤

Framework objective
Identify pairs of fractions that total 1

Vocabulary
fraction, unit fraction, mixed number, numerator, denominator, equivalent

Resources
Interactive activity: Fractions that make one whole

⑤ Fractions that make one whole

Show the children the interactive activity 'Fractions that make one whole'. In this activity they are asked to match pairs of fractions that add up to exactly one whole.

Teacher support
Less confident learners: Ask these children to use or devise an equivalence chart to help them with this task.
More confident learners: Challenge these children to write their own questions, similar to those featured in the interactive activity, for a partner to solve.

Common misconception
Children lack understanding about the significance of the numerator and the denominator.
Discuss the numerator and denominator by using fractions of shapes. Show that the denominator signifies the number of parts the whole is divided into. Therefore, the numerator must be of the same value to signify a whole (for example, $^3/_3$). Consequently, where two fractions that have the same denominator total 1, then the sum of the two numerators must be equal to the denominator.

Probing questions
● How many halves/eighths/quarters/thirds/sixths make one whole?
● $^3/_5 + \square/5 = 1$. Tell me a rule that you can use to work out the missing numerator.

Next steps
Support: Invite these children to shade fractions of circles and squares to show $^1/_3 + ^2/_3 = 1$, $^2/_5 + ^3/_5 = 1$ and so on. See also Year 4 Block E Unit 1.
Extension: Ask the children to explain their methods of working out to a partner. Encourage them to give additional examples of pairs of fractions that total 1, and present their findings to others. See also Year 4 Block E Unit 3

BLOCK E

Activity ⑥

Prior learning
Children can find unit fractions of numbers and quantities, such as $\frac{1}{2}$, $\frac{1}{3}$, $\frac{1}{4}$ and $\frac{1}{6}$ of 12 litres.

Framework objective
Find fractions of numbers, quantities or shapes (for example, $\frac{1}{5}$ of 30 plums, $\frac{3}{8}$ of a 6 by 4 rectangle)

Vocabulary
divide, divided by, multiply, multiplied by, fraction, numerator, denominator, equivalent

Resources
Worksheet: Fractions of quantities

⑥ Fractions of quantities

Hand out copies of the worksheet 'Fractions of quantities' for the children to complete.

Teacher support
Less confident learners: Remind these children of the link between division and the denominator to help them find unit fractions (for example, $\frac{1}{4}$ of 20 sweets = 20 ÷ 4). Then remind them that they can combine this with multiplication to find fractions with a numerator other than 1 (for example, $\frac{3}{5}$ of 10 cars = 10 ÷ 5 × 3).
More confident learners: Encourage these children to explain how they worked out their answers and to give further examples to their partner or group to solve.

Common misconception
Children lack a strategy for checking their answers.
Discuss with children the correct number operations to use and discuss how to use jottings and diagrams to check their answers. Ask children to give examples of how they have or are going to check answers.

Probing questions
● What is $\frac{1}{4}$ of 1000? What about $\frac{3}{4}$ of 1000? What number operations are you using to find these answers?
● How do you find $\frac{1}{5}$ of a number or quantity? And $\frac{4}{5}$?

Next steps
Support: Provide opportunities for these children to practise finding unit fractions of numbers and quantities. Discuss how division is being used. Ask what the next step is to find a multiple fraction (for example, $\frac{3}{5}$ as opposed to $\frac{1}{5}$). See also Year 4 Block E Unit 1.
Extension: Invite the children to find fractions of other quantities, such as money and time. Ask them to explain how to work out $\frac{2}{5}$ of a £1 in pence, $\frac{3}{4}$ of an hour in minutes, and so on. See also Year 4 Block E Unit 3.

BLOCK E

Unit 3 ◻ Securing number facts, relationships and counting

Introduction

In this unit, children continue to solve one- and two-step word problems involving numbers, money and measures. They represent problems and interpret solutions, using a calculator when appropriate. Children continue to develop their tables to 10 × 10. They refine and develop their written methods of multiplication and division. Finally, they investigate the equivalence of fractions, mixed numbers, fractions of shapes and quantities. They are also introduced to the language of ratio and proportion.

Framework objectives	Assessment focuses		Success criteria for Year 4	Learning outcomes
	Level 4	Level 3		
① Multiplication and division quizzes				
Derive and recall multiplication facts up to 10 × 10, the corresponding division facts and multiples of numbers to 10 up to the tenth multiple	• quickly derive division facts that correspond to multiplication facts up to 10 × 10 • recall multiplication facts up to 10 × 10 and quickly derive corresponding division facts	• derive associated division facts from known multiplication facts, e.g. ● given a number sentence, use understanding of operations to create related sentences • use mental recall of the 2, 3, 4, 5 and 10 multiplication tables	• can use all multiplication facts up to the tenth multiple, and corresponding division facts • can work out remainders when dividing	*I know all multiplication facts up to 10 × 10, even when they are not in the right order.*
② Multiplying and dividing – written methods				
Develop and use written methods to record, support and explain multiplication and division of two-digit numbers by a one-digit number, including division with remainders (e.g. 15 × 9, 98 ÷ 6)	• use efficient written methods of short multiplication and division	• multiply and divide two digit numbers by 2, 3, 4 or 5 as well as 10 with whole number answers and remainders, e.g. ● calculate 49 ÷ 3	● understands how to use a range of written methods of multiplication and division • able to explain the methods used	*I can use a written method to multiply a two-digit number by a one-digit number. I can use a written method to divide a two-digit number by a one-digit number and find the remainder.*

◼ SCHOLASTIC

Unit 3 ◰ Securing number facts, relationships and counting

Framework objectives	Assessment focuses		Success criteria for Year 4	Learning outcomes
	Level 4	Level 3		
③ Decimal and fraction equivalents				
Recognise the equivalence between decimal and fraction forms of one half, quarters, tenths and hundredths	• recognise approximate proportions of a whole and use simple fractions and percentages to describe these, e.g. ● recognise simple equivalence between fractions and decimals, e.g. $1/2$, $1/4$, $1/10$, $3/4$ • solve problems with or without a calculator, e.g. ● interpret a calculator display of 4.5 as £4.50 in context of money	• begin to use decimal notation in contexts such as money, e.g. ● order decimals with one dp, or two dp in context of money ● know that £3.06 equals 306p	• can identify the equivalent decimal and fraction forms of tenths, hundredths, half, quarters • investigates a range of equivalents that are linked to tenths, hundredths, half and quarters	*I know that $1/2$ can also be written as 0.5, $1/4$ as 0.25 and $3/4$ as 0.75. I know that one tenth can be written as $1/10$ or as 0.1 and that one hundredth can be written as $1/100$ or 0.01. I know that $25/100$ is the same as 0.25. It is also the same as $1/4$.*
④ Fraction equivalents				
Use diagrams to identify equivalent fractions (e.g. $6/8$ and $3/4$, or $70/100$ and $7/10$); interpret mixed numbers and position them on a number line (e.g. $3 1/2$)	• recognise approximate proportions of a whole and use simple fractions and percentages to describe these, e.g. ● recognise simple equivalence between fractions	• use simple fractions that are several parts of a whole and recognise when two simple fractions are equivalent, e.g. ● recognise and record fractions that are several parts of the whole such as $3/4$, $2/5$ ● recognise some fractions that are equivalent to $1/2$	• can identify equivalent fractions on a diagram • can order fractions and mixed numbers on a number line	*I can use a 2 by 5 rectangle to show you that one fifth is the same as two tenths. I can place mixed numbers in the correct place on a number line.*
⑤ Fractions and quantities				
Find fractions of numbers, quantities or shapes (e.g. $1/5$ of 30 plums, $3/8$ of a 6 by 4 rectangle)	• recognise approximate proportions of a whole and use simple fractions and percentages to describe these	• use simple fractions that are several parts of a whole and recognise when two simple fractions are equivalent, e.g. ● understand and use unit fractions such as $1/2$, $1/4$, $1/3$, $1/5$, $1/10$ and find those fractions of shapes and sets of objects ● recognise and record fractions	• can find fractions of quantities and measure and order them	*I can find the fraction of an amount, such as $2/5$ of £10.*

BLOCK E

Unit 3 📖 Securing number facts, relationships and counting

Framework objectives	Assessment focuses		Success criteria for Year 4	Learning outcomes
	Level 4	Level 3		
6 Puzzles and problems - ratio and proportion				
Represent a puzzle or problem using number sentences, statements or diagrams; use these to solve the problem; present and interpret the solution in the context of the problem	• present information and results in a clear and organised way, e.g. ○ organise written work, e.g. record results in order ○ begin to work in an organised way from the start ○ consider appropriate units ○ use related vocabulary accurately	• begin to organise their work and check results, e.g. ○ begin to develop own ways of recording ○ develop an organised approach as they get into recording their work on a problem • discuss their mathematical work and begin to explain their thinking, e.g. ○ use appropriate mathematical vocabulary ○ talk about their findings by referring to their written work • use and interpret mathematical symbols and diagrams	• uses number sentences, statements and drawings to help solve a problem • re-reads the question to make sure the answer makes sense • can work with others to discuss and plan how to solve a problem	*I can write down number sentences or drawings to help me solve a problem.* *When I have solved a problem I re-read the question to make sure that it makes sense.*
Use the vocabulary of ratio and proportion to describe the relationship between two quantities (e.g. 'There are 2 red beads to every 3 blue beads, or 2 beads in every 5 beads are red'); estimate a proportion (e.g. 'About one quarter of the apples in the box are green')	• begin to understand simple ratio	There is no assessment focus for this level	• begins to use and understand the vocabulary of ratio and proportion	*I can solve simple ratio and proportion problems.*

BLOCK E

📖 SCHOLASTIC

Activity ①

Prior learning
Children can recall multiplication facts and derive related division facts for the 2-, 3-, 4-, 5- and 10-times tables.

Framework objective
Derive and recall multiplication facts up to 10 × 10, the corresponding division facts and multiples of numbers to 10 up to the tenth multiple

Vocabulary
multiply, multiplied by, divide, divided by, remainder, multiple, divisor, remainder

Resources
Worksheets: Multiplication and division quizzes (1), (2) and (3)

① Multiplication and division quizzes

Hand out copies of the worksheet 'Multiplication and division quizzes (1)' and ask the children to complete it.

Teacher support
Less confident learners: Let these children start off by completing the worksheet 'Multiplication and division quizzes (2)'.
More confident learners: Ask these children to complete the worksheet 'Multiplication and division quizzes (3)'.

Common misconception
Children do not understand the language involved in multiplication and division. Read through the vocabulary list with children. Discuss and share examples of number facts to revise what is meant by each word.

Probing questions
● How can you work out 90 × 7 if you know 9 × 7?
● What is a good strategy for working out remainders when you are dividing?

Next steps
Support: Practise multiplication and division by chanting times tables with children and play 'pairs' games with question and answer cards (the children can prepare the cards themselves as extra practice). See also Year 4 Block E Unit 2.
Extension: Give the children a number and challenge them to write down as many multiplication and division facts relating to it as they can. See also Year 5 Block E Unit 1.

BLOCK E

Activity ②

Prior learning
Children can recall multiplication facts and derive related division facts for the 2-, 3-, 4-, 5- and 10-times tables. Some children may now be able to recall all facts up to 10 × 10.

Framework objective
Develop and use written methods to record, support and explain multiplication and division of two-digit numbers by a one-digit number, including division with remainders (for example, 15 × 9, 98 ÷ 6)

Vocabulary
multiply, multiplied by, divide, divided by, product, quotient, remainder, multiple, factor, divisor, divisible by

Resources
Display pages: Written multiplication, Written division
Worksheet: Multiplying and dividing – written methods
Resource sheet: 0–9 digit cards
Classroom resources: place value arrow cards

② Multiplying and dividing – written methods

Reveal the display pages 'Written multiplication' and 'Written division'. Go through the examples with the children before giving them copies of the worksheet 'Multiplying and dividing – written methods' to complete. Encourage them to check with a partner that they both understand how to use the methods shown. Now ask them to answer independently all the questions shown. When they have both finished their independent working they should check their methods and answers with their partner.

Teacher support
Less confident learners: To begin with, ask these children to work in a small group with an adult to revise the methods shown. They could continue to work through the sheet as a group if necessary. Observe how much each child can contribute to the task.
More confident learners: Encourage these children to demonstrate their understanding of the written methods by working with three-digit numbers with a one-digit multiplier or divisor.

Common misconception
Children use an inappropriate method to multiply or divide.
Encourage children to identify and use the most efficient written method for a particular multiplication or division calculation. Check that they fully understand the process involved.

Probing questions
● Why did you break the two-digit number down in this way?
● How can you check your answer to this multiplication/division problem?

Next steps
Support: Ask the children to use place value arrow cards to make two-digit numbers and multiply these by one-digit numbers picked at random from a set of digit cards. A partner can then check the written method that they have used. See also Year 4 Block A Unit 2 and Block D Unit 2.
Extension: Challenge these children to write multiplication and division word problems for a partner to solve. They should ensure that the calculations involved will require the use of a written method. See also Year 5 Block A Unit 2.

■SCHOLASTIC

BLOCK E

Activity ③

Prior learning
Children can read and write proper fractions as tenths and hundredths.

Framework objective
Recognise the equivalence between decimal and fraction forms of one half, quarters, tenths and hundredths

Vocabulary
fraction, decimal fraction, numerator, denominator, equivalent

Resources
Worksheet: Decimal and fraction equivalents
Classroom resources: blank number line

③ Decimal and fraction equivalents

Ask the children to complete the worksheet 'Decimal and fraction equivalents'. The 100-squares that they complete (showing hundredths and decimals) will help them to see the equivalence between fractions and decimals.

Teacher support
Less confident learners: Let these children work in a small group with an adult. Discuss the link between decimal fractions and fractions and the equivalence between tenths and hundredths.
More confident learners: Ask these children to find the decimal equivalent of $^1/_5$, $^2/_5$, $^3/_5$, $^4/_5$. Let them work with a less confident learner and explain their strategies and methods.

Common misconception
Children are confused between 0.1 and 0.01 and have difficulty recognising that 0.1 is the same as 0.10.
Ask children to look at 100-squares like those on the worksheet 'Decimal and fraction equivalents' with an adult or a more confident learner. It is also important to do lots of oral work so children get used to the language of decimals and fractions.

Probing questions
● How many ways can you write ½ as both an equivalent fraction and as a decimal fraction? ($^5/_{10}$, 0.5, $^{50}/_{100}$, 0.50)
● Show me how to write $^7/_{100}$ as a decimal fraction. What about $^{17}/_{100}$?

Next steps
Support: Provide opportunities for these children to practise using decimals in the context of money. See also Year 4 Block E Units 1 and 2.
Extension: Provide the children with a blank number line. Ask them to fill in all twenty divisions between 0 and 2, writing both decimals and their fraction equivalents (that is, 0, 0.1 and $^1/_{10}$, 0.2 and $^2/_{10}$ (or $^1/_5$) and so on). See also Year 5 Block E Unit 1.

BLOCK E

Activity ④

Prior learning
Children can recall multiplication facts and derive related division facts for the 2-, 3-, 4-, 5- and 10-times tables. They can read and write proper fractions. They understand the terms 'denominator' (the parts of a whole) and 'numerator' (the number of parts).

Framework objective
Use diagrams to identify equivalent fractions (for example, $6/8$ and $3/4$, or $70/100$ and $7/10$); interpret mixed numbers and position them on a number line (for example, $3^1/_2$).

Vocabulary
fraction, unit fraction, decimal fraction, mixed number, numerator, denominator, equivalent

Resources
Worksheet: Fraction equivalents
Resource sheets: Multiplication square, Blank 100-square

④ Fraction equivalents

If necessary, ensure that the children are confident with the necessary vocabulary (particularly that they understand the term 'equivalent' and know how to find equivalents). Ask them to read through the worksheet 'Fraction equivalents' in pairs to see if they understand the tasks. The children should complete the sheet independently, and then be prepared to explain their working to others.

Teacher support
Less confident learners: Ask these children to work in a group with an adult and practise finding equivalent fractions with simple examples. Then ask them to attempt the worksheet 'Fraction equivalents'.
More confident learners: Challenge these children to extend the number line in question 10 on the worksheet to 5 and give them more decimal fractions to place on it. They might also produce number lines in thirds.

Common misconception
Children have difficulty finding equivalent fractions.
Remind children to multiply or divide both the numerator and the denominator by the same number. If necessary, provide a multiplication square to give extra confidence.

Probing questions
● How many equivalents of ¼ and ¾ can you think of? Write them down.

Next steps
Support: Provide these children with further practice in finding equivalents and give them access to a multiplication square to help them. See also Year 4 Block E Units 1 and 2.
Extension: Give these children a blank 100-square and ask them to create a diagram to show they understand the equivalents of tenths and hundredths. See also Year 5 Block E Unit 1.

Activity ⑤

Prior learning
Children can find unit fractions of numbers and quantities (for example, $\frac{1}{2}$, $\frac{1}{3}$, $\frac{1}{4}$ and $\frac{1}{6}$ of 12 litres).

Framework objective
Find fractions of numbers, quantities or shapes (for example, $\frac{1}{5}$ of 30 plums, $\frac{3}{8}$ of a 6 by 4 rectangle)

Vocabulary
divide, divided by, multiply, multiplied by, fraction, numerator, denominator, equivalent

Resources
Interactive activity: Fractions and quantities

⑤ Fractions and quantities

Show the children the interactive activity 'Fractions and quantities'. In this activity the children are asked to order a list of quantities, starting with the largest at the top and finishing with the smallest at the bottom.

Teacher support
Less confident learners: Remind these children of the link between division and fractions, and how to use multiplication to find fractions other than unit fractions.
More confident learners: Invite these children to explain how they worked out their answers and to give further examples to their partner or group to solve.

Common misconception
Children are insecure at calculating fractions of quantities.
Practise finding fractions of numbers and discuss the processes involved in such calculations. Encourage children to use jottings. Then move on to finding fraction of measures.

Probing questions
● What is $\frac{2}{5}$ of 150? And $\frac{3}{4}$ of 72? What number operations are you using to find these answers?
● If you know half of a number, how can you then find a quarter and an eighth?

Next steps
Support: Provide opportunities for these children to continue to practise finding unit fractions of numbers and quantities. Discuss how division is being used. Ask what the next step is to find a multiple fraction (for example, $\frac{3}{8}$ as opposed to $\frac{1}{8}$). See also Year 4 Block E Units 1 and 2.
Extension: Challenge the children to write word problems that involve finding fractions of quantities. Their partners can then solve these. See also Year 5 Block E Unit 1.

BLOCK E

Activity ⑥

Prior learning
Children can identify the calculation needed to solve a one-step problem. They compare solutions with others' and identify the best approaches.

Framework objectives
● Represent a puzzle or problem using number sentences, statements or diagrams; use these to solve the problem; present and interpret the solution in the context of the problem
● Use the vocabulary of ratio and proportion to describe the relationship between two quantities (for example, 'There are 2 red beads to every 3 blue beads, or 2 beads in every 5 beads are red'); estimate a proportion (for example, 'About one quarter of the apples in the box are green')

Vocabulary
problem, solution, answer, method, explain, add, subtract, multiply, divide, proportion, in every, for every, to every

Resources
Worksheet: Puzzles and problems – ratio and proportion
Classroom resources: coloured cubes, beads and string

⑥ Puzzles and problems – ratio and proportion

Divide the class into small groups or pairs to do this activity. It is important that the children are able to discuss and interpret the problems with each other and that you are able to listen and observe. Ask them to complete the worksheet 'Puzzles and problems – ratio and proportion' in their groups or pairs.

Teacher support
Less confident learners: Ask these children to work in a group with an adult who can prompt if and when necessary. Use coloured cubes to represent boys/girls, apples/pears, and so on, to assist in producing diagrams and solutions.
More confident learners: After the children have completed the worksheet, ask them to write similar problems to present to the rest of the group.

Common misconception
Children are insecure with the vocabulary of ratio and proportion (for example, thinking that 1 in every 2 does not mean $^1/_2$ but $^1/_3$)
Work in a practical way using cubes. Combining the use of diagrams with the corresponding language under adult guidance will help children become familiar with the required language.

Probing questions
● Using your diagram, show me that your answer is correct.
● Show me how you checked your work.

Next steps
Support: Provide lots of practical work in groups and pairs using diagrams and concrete materials such as cubes to reinforce ideas about ratio and proportion. Use earlier problem-solving questions from any Year 4 block to give children the confidence to have a go at finding solutions and checking their own work in pairs or groups. Also provide them with suitable opportunities to present their results to others.
Extension: Provide coloured beads and strings. Challenge the children to make 'necklaces' of repeating patterns of beads and to write a ratio and proportion statement for each. See also Year 5 Block E Unit 2.

Periodic assessment

These activities can be used at any time during the teaching of this block to assess those children that you think have achieved the objective. A grid highlighting the related assessment focuses and expected learning outcomes for each activity can be found on the CD-ROM.

How many facts?

Framework objective
Derive and recall multiplication facts up to 10 × 10, the corresponding division facts and multiples of numbers to 10 up to the tenth multiple

Learning outcomes
● I can tell you answers to the 2-, 3-, 4-, 5-, 6- and 10-times tables, even when they are not in the right order.
● I can recall multiplication facts to 10 × 10 and quickly say the corresponding division facts.
● If you give me a multiplication fact I can give you one or two division facts to go with it.

Ask the children to complete the first question on the worksheet 'How many facts?' They have to write as many multiplication and division facts as they can find for each of the given numbers. You may decide to set a time limit. Once they have done this, ask them to complete the second question. This will help you to assess their understanding of inverse operations.

Finding equivalent fractions

Framework objective
Use diagrams to identify equivalent fractions (e.g. $^6/_8$ and $^3/_4$, or $^{70}/_{100}$ and $^7/_{10}$); interpret mixed numbers and position them on a number line (e.g. $3^1/_2$)

Learning outcome
● I can show you on a diagram of a rectangle made from eight squares that one half is the same as two quarters or four eighths.

Ask the children to complete the worksheet 'Finding equivalent fractions' to show their understanding of fractions, equivalents and mixed numbers.

Written methods for multiplication and division

Framework objective
Develop and use written methods to record, support and explain multiplication and division of two-digit numbers by a one-digit number, including division with remainders

Learning outcomes
● I can use a written method to multiply a two-digit number by a one-digit number.
● I can use a written method to divide a two-digit number by a one-digit number and find the remainder.

Ask the children to complete the worksheet 'Written methods for multiplication and division' to show their understanding of written methods of multiplication and division, including division with remainders.

BLOCK E

Name	Date

How many facts?

1. a) How many multiplication and division facts can you find for each of the following numbers? Your teacher may decide to give you a time limit.

42	
72	
18	
100	
36	
54	
36	
24	
9	
20	

b) Use these numbers to show a division with a remainder.

$32 \div ? = ?$
$19 \div ? = ?$
$41 \div ? = ?$
$56 \div ? = ?$
$65 \div ? = ?$

Name	Date

(continued)

2. Answer these questions. For each calculation:

(i) work out the answer

(ii) write an inverse operation.

a) (i) $6 \times 10 =$ _____ (ii) _____

b) (i) $4 \times 9 =$ _____ (ii) _____

c) (i) $7 \times 6 =$ _____ (ii) _____

d) (i) $8 \times 3 =$ _____ (ii) _____

e) (i) $5 \times 8 =$ _____ (ii) _____

Now make up five examples of your own:

f) (i) _____ (ii) _____

g) (i) _____ (ii) _____

h) (i) _____ (ii) _____

i) (i) _____ (ii) _____

j) (i) _____ (ii) _____

How easy?

Red

Amber

Green

How do you think you have done?

_____

_____

Name   Date

Finding equivalent fractions

Rectangle 1

1. Look at the shape below. What fraction of the large rectangle is each small rectangle?

_____

2. Colour half of the large rectangle. How many parts have you coloured?

_____

3. What is another way to write $\frac{1}{2}$ when you say how many you have coloured?

_____

Rectangle 2

1. Colour three of the small rectangles in the large rectangle above. What fraction of the whole shape have you coloured?

_____

2. What fraction is not coloured? _____

Name	Date

(continued)

Rectangle 3

1. Colour $\frac{1}{4}$ of the rectangle above. What other ways could you write the fraction you have coloured?

_____

2. What fraction is not coloured? Write your answer in three different ways.

_____

■ Order the following fractions and mixed numbers from the smallest to the largest:

1. $\frac{7}{10}$, $\frac{2}{5}$, $\frac{3}{5}$, $\frac{1}{5}$, $1\frac{1}{2}$, $\frac{1}{2}$, 2, $\frac{1}{10}$, $\frac{9}{10}$

_____

2. $\frac{3}{4}$, $\frac{1}{4}$, $\frac{1}{2}$, $1\frac{1}{4}$, $1\frac{1}{8}$, $1\frac{3}{4}$, $\frac{1}{8}$, $1\frac{1}{2}$, 2

_____

BLOCK E

How easy?

Red
Amber
Green

How do you think you have done?

_____

_____

Name		Date

Written methods for division and multiplication

■ Use the grids to complete these multiplication questions.

1. 14 × 7 = _____

×	7
10	
4	

2. 15 × 6 = _____

×	6
10	
5	

3. 23 × 5 = _____

×	5
20	
3	

4. 28 × 4 = _____

×	4
20	
8	

5.   33 × 9 = _____

×	9
30	
3	

■ Now choose your own written method to work out the answers to the following questions.

6. 18 × 4 = _____

7. 27 × 6 = _____

8. 45 × 6 = _____

9. 36 × 5 = _____

10. 72 × 8 = _____

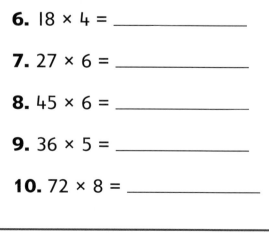

BLOCK E

Name	Date

(continued)

◼ For each of these division calculations:

a) show a written method of calculating the answer (the first one has been started for you)

b) show an inverse operation that you can use to check your working out.

1. a) $29 \div 3 \quad = (20 + 9) \div 3$

$\qquad = (20 \div 3) + (\underline{\hspace{2cm}})$

$\qquad = 6 \, r \, 2 + \underline{\hspace{1cm}}$

$\qquad \underline{\hspace{3cm}}$

b) _____

2. a) $37 \div 6 =$ _____

_____

_____

_____

b) _____

3. a) $58 \div 5 =$ _____

_____

_____

_____

b) _____

How easy?

Red ⚫

Amber ⚫

Green ⚫

How do you think you have done?

_____

_____

BLOCK E

Transitional assessment

Activity	Type	Level	Description
3.1a 3.1b	Single-level written assessments	3	Two 20-minute formal test papers covering objectives from all Strands of the Framework at Level 3 (one calculator, one non-calculator)
3.2a 3.2b	Single-level written assessments	3	Two 20-minute formal test papers covering objectives from all Strands of the Framework at Level 3 (one calculator, one non-calculator)
3.3a 3.3b	Single-level written assessments	3	Two 20-minute formal test papers covering objectives from all Strands of the Framework at Level 3 (one calculator, one non-calculator)
3.4	Single-level oral assessment	3	Approximately 5-minute oral paper covering objectives from all Strands of the Framework at Level 3
3.5	Single-level oral assessment	3	Approximately 5-minute oral paper covering objectives from all Strands of the Framework at Level 3
4.1a 4.1b	Single-level written assessments	4	Two 20-minute formal test papers covering objectives from all Strands of the Framework at Level 4 (one calculator, one non-calculator)
4.2a 4.2b	Single-level written assessments	4	Two 20-minute formal test papers covering objectives from all Strands of the Framework at Level 4 (one calculator, one non-calculator)
4.3a 4.3b	Single-level written assessments	4	Two 20-minute formal test papers covering objectives from all Strands of the Framework at Level 4 (one calculator, one non-calculator)
4.4	Single-level oral assessment	4	Approximately 5-minute oral paper covering objectives from all Strands of the Framework at Level 4
4.5	Single-level oral assessment	4	Approximately 5-minute oral paper covering objectives from all Strands of the Framework at Level 4

SCHOLASTIC

Written test instructions

Allow 20 minutes for each paper.

Children should work so that they cannot see each other's work.

Do not explain questions or read numbers to the children.

Teachers may choose to read the questions aloud to children, if they feel it is appropriate.

The test may be administered to groups of children or to the whole class.

The total marks available for each paper are given in the mark scheme.

Say to the children:

Here are some questions (I am going to read some questions) for you to answer.

For some questions you will write your answer in a box. [Show example.]

For some questions you may need to draw lines or rings to show your answer. [Show example.]

If you make a mistake, you should cross it out (or rub it out neatly) and write your answer clearly.

You may use spaces on the paper to do any working out that may help you.

Try to work out the answer to each question before going on to the next one.

If you can't answer a question, move on to the next one - it may be easier.

Equipment for each child

pencil, eraser (or children may cross out mistakes), 30cm ruler (marked in mm), mirror, tracing paper, protractor

Oral test instructions

Read questions to the children no more than twice.

Allow time allocated on each paper for each question: 5, 10 or 15 seconds.

Children record their answers on paper.

1 mark per question: 15 or 20 marks in total

Equipment for each child

pencil, eraser (or children may cross out mistakes), 30cm ruler

Separate teacher resources are listed for each paper.

Levelling the children

Add together the marks from an oral test and a combined mark for both written tests A and B.

Level 3		Level 4	
Below Level 3	0 - 21 marks	Below Level 4	0 - 21 marks
Low Level 3	22 - 31 marks	Low Level 4	22 - 31 marks
Secure Level 3	32 - 40 marks	Secure Level 4	32 - 40 marks
High Level 3	40 - 50 marks	High Level 4	40 - 50 marks

When awarding an end-of-year Teacher Assessment Level, teachers also need to consider a child's performance on Periodic and Day-to-Day Assessments.

Mathematics: making a level judgement

Use these steps to formalise your assessments of pupils' mathematics into level judgements.

You will need
- evidence of the pupil's mathematics that shows most independence, for example from work in other subjects as well as in mathematics lessons
- other evidence about the pupil as a mathematician, for example notes on plans, the pupil's own reflections, your own recollections of classroom interactions, oral answers given during mental starters
- a copy of the assessment guidelines for the level borderline that is your starting point.

Step 1 Making best fit judgements
Within each assessment focus, draw on the pupil's work and other evidence including what you know about the pupil's mathematics. Use the criteria in the assessment guidelines to decide which level provides the best fit.

↓

Step 2 Work through Ma2 Number
Begin with the assessment guidelines for Ma2 Number.

Look at the criteria within each AF. Decide which level describes the pupil best.

Record the level for each AF in the appropriate box.

Record 'insufficient evidence' (IE) if you do not know enough about this aspect of the pupil's mathematics to make a judgement. This has implications for planning.

If you feel the pupil is operating below the level, check the criteria on the assessment guidelines for the level below.

↓

Step 3 Making an overall level judgement for Ma2 Number
Now make your level decision for Ma2 Number.

- Your AF judgements give an impression of the best fit level for Ma2.
- Read the complete level descriptions for both levels to confirm your impression of the best fit level for Ma2

Decide whether the level is Low, Secure or High. Do this by thinking about what the pupil demonstrates:
- how much of the level
- how consistently
- how independently
- in what range of contexts.

Tick the relevant Low, Secure or High box for the level.

↓

Step 4 Repeat the process for Ma3, Ma4 and then Ma1
For the Ma1 judgement, consider how the pupil uses and applies the mathematics of Ma2, Ma3 and Ma4.

APP

Name	Date

Activity name _____

Objective:
Learning outcome:
Comments:

Self-assessment

How well did you do this? _____

_____

_____

_____

What do you still need to do? _____

_____

_____

_____

How easy?

Red

Amber

Green

How do you think you have done? _____

_____

APP

SCHOLASTIC

Also available in this series:

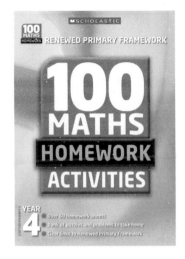

100 MATHS ASSESSMENT LESSONS Y1
ISBN 978-1407-10183-5

100 MATHS FRAMEWORK LESSONS Y1
ISBN 978-0439-94546-2

100 MATHS HOMEWORK ACTIVITIES Y1
ISBN 978-1407-10216-0

100 MATHS ASSESSMENT LESSONS Y2
ISBN 978-1407-10184-2

100 MATHS FRAMEWORK LESSONS Y2
ISBN 978-0439-94547-9

100 MATHS HOMEWORK ACTIVITIES Y2
ISBN 978-1407-10217-7

100 MATHS ASSESSMENT LESSONS Y3
ISBN 978-1407-10185-9

100 MATHS FRAMEWORK LESSONS Y3
ISBN 978-0439-94548-6

100 MATHS HOMEWORK ACTIVITIES Y3
ISBN 978-1407-10218-4

100 MATHS ASSESSMENT LESSONS Y4
ISBN 978-1407-10192-7

100 MATHS FRAMEWORK LESSONS Y4
ISBN 978-0439-94549-3

100 MATHS HOMEWORK ACTIVITIES Y4
ISBN 978-1407-10219-1

100 MATHS ASSESSMENT LESSONS Y5
ISBN 978-1407-10193-4

100 MATHS FRAMEWORK LESSONS Y5
ISBN 978-0439-94550-9

100 MATHS HOMEWORK ACTIVITIES Y5
ISBN 978-1407-10220-7

100 MATHS ASSESSMENT LESSONS Y6
ISBN 978-1407-10194-1

100 MATHS FRAMEWORK LESSONS Y6
ISBN 978-0439-94551-6

100 MATHS HOMEWORK ACTIVITIES Y6
ISBN 978-1407-10221-4

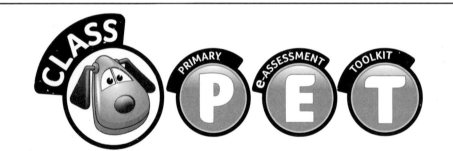

The easy-to-use online assessment solution for primary schools!
Class PET helps you to use *100 Assessment Lessons* across the whole school!

Class PET contains all of the *100 Assessment Lessons* content as well as a wealth of additional assessment resources. It is designed to help you assess pupils' performance and personalise and enrich the teaching and learning cycle. *Class PET* includes:

- 100s of ready-made, high-quality electronic assessments
- Primary-friendly features to support self- and peer-assessment
- A personalised 'Learning Blog' to capture targets and comments from pupils, peers, parents and teachers
- Extremely flexible assessment, reporting and tracking – carefully designed to work with the way you teach
- Interactive teaching materials from *100 Assessment Lessons*, including on-screen activities and teacher tools, lesson notes and editable planning grids
- Online and in line with the needs of the busy classroom teacher, and ideal for APP!

Perfect for APP!

ONLINE **For further information, visit www.scholastic.co.uk/classpet**